TOM FALUDI

D0364678

GREAT MEN OF
SCIENCE

GREAT MEN OF SCIENCE

BY ARNOLD DOLIN

ILLUSTRATED BY RAFAELLO BUSONI

Hart Publishing Company

NEW YORK CITY

ALL RIGHTS RESERVED
Including the right of representation in whole or in part or in any form
Copyright © 1960 by Hart Publishing Company
New York 11, N. Y.
Manufactured in the United States of America

Library of Congress Catalog Card No. 60-6576

DESIGNED BY STEFAN SALTER

CONTENTS

Hippocrates	9
Archimedes	15
Copernicus	20
Andreas Vesalius	24
Galileo Galilei	32
Johannes Kepler	37
William Harvey	41
Antony van Leeuwenhoek	47
Isaac Newton	58
Antoine Lavoisier	62
Alessandro Volta	71
Charles Goodyear	74
Michael Faraday	79
William Morton	86
Charles Darwin	95
Louis Pasteur	105
Joseph Lister	115
Alexander Graham Bell	124
Thomas Alva Edison	129
Walter Reed	139
Luther Burbank	146
The Curies	153
George Washington Carver	162
The Wright Brothers	175
Frederick Banting	182
Albert Einstein	189

List of Illustrations

HIPPOCRATES
"You are now doctors . . . Be true to your oath . . ."   11

ARCHIMEDES
"Eureka! I have found it!"   19

COPERNICUS
He claimed . . . the earth moved in an orbit.   22

ANDREAS VESALIUS
"It's not right to cut up human flesh . . .!"   27
"You have committed heresy . . ."   30

GALILEO-GALILEI
. . . both balls hit the ground at the same moment.   35

JOHANNES KEPLER
Johannes spent his spare time studying astronomy   39

WILLIAM HARVEY
"Your Majesty . . . the heart is a pump!"   45

ANTONY VAN LEEUWENHOEK
Passers-by saw him bent over his microscopes.   51
. . . the Queen of England came to look . . .   55

ISAAC NEWTON
"Why . . . does the apple fall down?"   60

ANTOINE LAVOISIER
The soldiers led Lavoisier to prison.   64
"Off with his head!"   67

ALESSANDRO VOLTA
. . . to make a dead frog's legs kick . . .   72

CHARLES GOODYEAR
"Look!" The rubber isn't melting at all."   77

MICHAEL FARADAY
One day a fine gentleman came into the shop . . .   83

WILLIAM MORTON
    "I have a toothache . . ."   89
    "Gentlemen, this is no humbug!"   93
CHARLES DARWIN
    "Charles Darwin reporting for the voyage, sir."   99
    Darwin was amazed at the strange animals.   102
LOUIS PASTEUR
    Each of the twenty-five sheep . . gamboled about.   108
    "Get him quickly to the Pasteur laboratory!"   113
JOSEPH LISTER
    The surgeon is wearing an old black frock coat . .   117
    Jimmy . . . jumped out of bed and danced . . .   122
ALEXANDER GRAHAM BELL
    . . . he spoke the first actual telephone message.   127
THOMAS ALVA EDISON
    The operators . . . congratulated the young man.   132
    . . . the windows . . . suddenly blazed into light.   136
WALTER REED
    ". . . and you will kill off yellow fever."   141
    . . . three of the most heroic men in the world.   144
LUTHER BURBANK
    . . . grew hundreds of varieties on a single tree!   151
THE CURIES
    The tiny bit of matter glowed!   157
    . . . Marie . . . visited in the battle zones.   160
GEORGE WASHINGTON CARVER
    He taught them how to plant crops . . .   167
    Carver set up a School on Wheels.   173
THE WRIGHT BROTHERS
    . . . the machine . . . actually flew!   178
FREDERICK BANTING
    "Fred! Fred! It worked!"   187
ALBERT EINSTEIN
    . . . one of Nature's greatest secrets . . .   190

HIPPOCRATES

(450-359 B.C. or 377? B.C.)

Father of Medicine

ΊΠΠΟΚΡΑΤΗΣ

STANDING STRAIGHT and tall in their flowing white robes, the serious-faced young men listened to their beloved teacher, the great doctor, Hippocrates. Then, one by one, each young Greek stepped forward and proclaimed in a clear voice:

"I swear . . . so far as the power and discernment shall be mine, I will carry out a regimen for the benefit of the sick and will keep them from harm and wrong. To none will I give a deadly drug . . . Into whatever house I shall enter I shall go for the benefit of the sick."

Hippocrates spoke quietly to his students:

"You are now doctors. Never forget the meaning of the pledge you have given. Be true to your oath

9

and you will be true to your duties to your fellow men."

The pledge the young Greek doctors gave 2,500 years ago is called the Hippocratic Oath. To this very day, graduating medical students must swear to abide by that oath before becoming doctors.

But even if the Hippocratic Oath had not been an inspiration to doctors since ancient times, Hippocrates

"*You are now doctors . . . Be true to your oath . . .*"

would still rank high in the history of medicine. For he, almost single-handedly, made medicine a science.

In Hippocrates' time, the Greeks believed that people became sick only because the gods on lofty Mount Olympus were angry with them. No one imagined that there were different kinds of diseases—like measles, or chicken pox, or the mumps. All illnesses were thought to be part of one disease—and disease was the gods' way of punishing disobedient mortals.

Many men called themselves doctors. But they were doctors in name only. Since it was the gods who made people sick or well, a physician could not do much to help. The best way to cure a disease was not to treat the poor suffering patient—but to make a sacrifice to the gods.

Hippocrates, unlike any doctor before him, refused to ask the gods for aid. Instead, he dared to say:

"Sickness is not caused by the gods! It happens because there is something diseased in a man's body. Making sacrifices can do no good. Only by finding the natural cause of the disease from which the man suffers —and treating it with care—can he be cured."

When the superstitious ancients heard this blasphemy, they were aghast!

"Hippocrates will be struck down by a lightning bolt!" warned the priests in the marble temples. "He is daring the gods to do their worst! All of his patients—if he can find any—will surely die!"

At first, no sick person would trust himself to this foolish doctor who dared challenge the all-powerful gods. Then, as time passed, stories about Hippocrates began to be heard—stories of how men and women who seemed doomed had recovered under his care.

There was the case of the pale young man with hollow cheeks. The gods must have been very angry with him, for he could not stop his terrible coughing. Hippocrates studied the symptoms of this malady—then he prescribed his remedy:

"Go to the green hills outside the city," he told the young man. "Get as much rest and sunshine as you can and you will be cured."

Modern physicians call the sickness the young Greek suffered from *tuberculosis.* Today, they prescribe essentially the same treatment as Hippocrates did almost 2,500 years ago.

It was not long before even the most cynical changed their minds about Hippocrates.

"This doctor has some queer ideas," they said, "but maybe . . . maybe he's not so foolish after all." More and more sick people went to Hippocrates for help instead of appealing to the gods.

The great physician became renowned throughout all of ancient Greece. Students came to sit at the feet of this man who was the first to learn the basic facts about disease.

Hippocrates welcomed the young men who came to

study with him. He taught them all he knew. Better still, he showed them how to be guided by nature in the treatment of the sick.

"Do not think the doctor is all-knowing," he cautioned. "Always remember that the physician is only nature's helper."

Hippocrates also taught that practice makes perfect —in medicine as in most other things. He insisted that only doctors who were "able, speedy, painless, and always ready for an emergency" should perform surgical operations.

One day, when his students gathered to hear him, Hippocrates revealed his innermost thoughts about the future of medicine.

"Long after I'm gone, you and those doctors who follow you must add to mankind's knowledge about disease," he said. "Each one of us lives but for a short time, but the art of medicine is eternal. Let us all contribute what we can, so that medicine may progress."

Hippocrates died at the age of seventy, surrounded by devoted disciples. He had written more than a hundred medical books during his lifetime—books which were to instruct and guide doctors for generations to come. His many students spread his teachings throughout the civilized world.

Through the genius and courage of this fearless trailblazer, medicine was freed of superstition and became a science.

ARCHIMEDES

(287?-212 B.C.)

Greatest Scientist of the Ancient World

"I DESIRE a crown," said Hiero, King of Syracuse, to his royal goldsmith. "It is to be an offering of thanks to the gods and must be fashioned from the purest gold. Do my bidding and you shall be well rewarded."

But when the royal jeweler brought the crown for the king's approval, Hiero was suspicious. One of his courtiers had warned him that the goldsmith was dishonest; perhaps the gold in the crown had been mixed with baser metal.

If the king offered an impure crown to the gods, the gods would be wroth. What revenge might they not take on the Kingdom of Syracuse?

Yet the crown *looked* as if it were made of gold. How could one prove that it contained silver?

"Call Archimedes, the mathematician," commanded Hiero. "Only he will be able to tell me about the crown."

Archimedes felt honored at the king's summons, but accepted it nevertheless with gravity. In that day and age, no one in all the world knew how to solve the problem posed by Hiero's crown.

So concerned was Archimedes with the problem that he thought about it day and night—even when he was preparing to take his bath. Suddenly, as he was getting into the tub, the solution to the problem came to him in a flash. He was so overjoyed that he dashed into the streets shouting, "Eureka! Eureka! I have found it! I have found it!"

Archimedes had noticed that, as he immersed his body in the bath, the water rose in the tub and ran over the sides. What happened was that the bulk of his body was taking the place of a certain amount of water.

"Of course!" he thought. "Different materials have different weights. Since gold is heavier than silver, a pound of gold must be smaller in size—less massive—than a pound of silver. Consequently, if I place a piece of gold weighing one pound in my tub, it will displace less water than a bulkier piece of silver weighing exactly the same."

The principle once clear, Archimedes was sure that he could perform an experiment to prove whether

Hiero's crown was pure gold or not. He knew that a pure gold crown would displace less water than a crown of the same weight, made of a combination of silver and gold.

First, the mathematician weighed the crown. Then, he ordered from the king's treasury a piece of gold of exactly the same weight as the alleged gold crown.

Now he filled a container brimful of water, and put the crown into it. The water that overflowed was caught in a basin, the water carefully measured, and the amount noted. Next, he refilled the self-same container to the top. This time, he put the piece of pure gold into the water. As before, he collected the water that overflowed, measured that, and noted the amount.

"Now," said Archimedes, "the crown and the piece of gold were the same weight. If the crown were pure gold it would have displaced exactly the same amount of water as did the pure gold from the king's treasury."

"Aha!" exclaimed Archimedes, "the king's jeweler is a thief—a fraud—a cheat! Water displaced by the piece of pure gold is less than the overflow caused by the crown—therefore there must be less gold in the crown than there is in the test piece of pure metal taken from the king's treasury. Both the crown and the test piece weigh the same: if both metals were really the same, each one would have displaced an equal amount of water. It is therefore clear that the king's jeweler introduced some baser metal—a metal of

lesser weight than gold—into the crown."

The king, provided with certain proof, was convinced. The goldsmith was punished and Archimedes was rewarded.

But his greatest reward had already come to him; he had discovered a new scientific principle. Today, this principle is formally established in many industrial and scientific uses.

By this and many other experiments and studies, Archimedes, the *Greatest Scientist of the Ancient World,* built the foundation of the modern science of physics.

"Eureka! I have found it!"

COPERNICUS

(1473-1543)

Discoverer of How Planets Move

WHEN COPERNICUS lived, in the 1500's, most scholars believed that the sun and the stars and the planets all revolved about the earth. It seemed logical to believe this. For the earth, to our limited senses, certainly doesn't seem to move, whereas the sun and the heavenly bodies seem to change their positions in the heavens.

Copernicus was not content. The accepted theory did not explain, for instance, what caused the change of the seasons.

Copernicus got the idea that the earth turned on an axis and that it also traveled around the sun. His friends told him he was crazy.

"How could the earth be spinning around?" they

said. "If that were true, when you jumped into the air you would come down in another spot!"

But Copernicus was an excellent student of mathematics. According to mathematical calulations, his theories were borne out. He studied and checked his ideas for many years. Then he wrote a book explaining all his findings.

When this book was published, it shocked and angered many people. They were angry not only because his ideas were different from what they had believed in for so long, but because the very idea that the earth was not the center of the universe seemed irreligious. For them, it was God's law and God's wish for the earth to be the most important planet. Didn't it say in the Bible that Man was "made in the image of God"? Would God put Man on some secondary planet? Impossible!

Now what exactly did Copernicus mean when he said that the earth spins on its axis? Let us suppose that you took an orange. Suppose you took a lollypop stick and stuck it through the center of the orange. If you twirled that orange on the stick, the orange would be spinning on its axis. In much the same way, the earth spins on its axis as it whirls through space.

It is this spinning motion which produces the phenomenon of day and night. The earth spins on its axis and makes a complete revolution once each day. When the Eastern Hemisphere faces the sun, then the West-

*Copernicus . . . claimed . . . the earth moved in an
orbit around the sun.*

ern Hemisphere is in the darkness of night. Conversely, when the spinning motion brings the Western Hemisphere to face the sun, then the Eastern Hemisphere experiences night.

Copernicus also claimed that the earth moved in an orbit around the sun. What is an orbit? Let us suppose that you have a maypole. Now, let us assume that children stand at equal distances from the maypole and dance around it. When they move around the maypole, they can be said to move in the same way that the earth moves around the sun. It is this motion of the earth, moving in its orbit around the sun, which produces the seasons.

According to the Copernican theory, the earth has at least two motions moving around the sun. It spins on its axis and, while it is spinning, it moves around the sun in a given orbit.

Of course, this was a most revolutionary theory in those days. Because of the ignorance of most people, Copernicus was not given, during his lifetime, the understanding and honor he deserved. Just a handful of progressive thinkers appreciated how brilliant and true his ideas were. But today, Nicholas Copernicus, the Polish scientist, is considered one of the world's great men.

ANDREAS VESALIUS

(1514-1564)

Father of Modern Anatomy

IT WAS THE year 1537. The university auditorium was crowded with medical students, physicians, professors, and curious townspeople. Excitement mounted, minute by minute. An elderly merchant remarked to the doctor sitting beside him, "They say he's only 23 years old. Can that be true?"

"Yes, but this youth can still teach us very much," answered his friend. "Why, he not only *lectures* on anatomy, but he actually shows us *proof* of his theories—shows us the proof in the bodies he cuts apart before our very eyes."

Just then, young Andreas Vesalius appeared on the platform, ready to begin his demonstration. There were murmurs of approval, amidst a respectful applause, but after the hall had become quiet, a clear, angry voice rang out: "It's not right to cut up human flesh like that!"

All eyes turned on the dark, scowling figure of a man clothed all in black. Again the man spoke: "Yes, even the souls of dead criminals have the right to rest in peace!"

In another part of the auditorium, an old crone raised a bony finger and shrilled, "You will bring suffering upon us all, meddling with the evil spirits of the dead!"

"Throw out those troublemakers!" some shouted in the excitement that had now laid hold of the audience. But Andreas Vesalius remained calm. He raised his arms for silence, and began to speak: "The human body is a fabric, a wonderful structure according to the work of the Supreme Creator and the Divine Artist, Nature. I want to describe it, with perfect truth and with perfect exactness. Can I do this by cutting apart monkeys and dogs and pigs? Is this how we can learn about man? The future of medicine and surgery depends upon our knowledge of our *own* bodies—not the bodies of dogs."

As he skillfully dissected the cadaver, a sense of wonder and awe crept over the audience. For the first time, the inside of a man was laid bare before them. They saw muscles, tissues, arteries and veins, and organs like the heart and the liver. And always, there

was the confident, patient voice of Andreas Vesalius
carefully explaining the function of each, and how it
fit into the total structure of the body.

Where had this dedicated, brilliant man come from?
Andreas was a Belgian—and his father, his grandfather, his great-grandfather, and even his great-great-
grandfather before him had all been distinguished doctors. His scientific interests were a family tradition.

As a boy, Andreas had had little time for childhood
games. He had been too busy dissecting every dead
animal he could find—mice, cats, toads, and vermin.
Andreas just wanted to learn all he could about the
parts of the body—muscles, bones, nerves, organs. And
he worked with whatever he could find.

When the time for more advanced study came,
young Vesalius went off to the Sorbonne University in
Paris. And it was in that great institution that Andreas
began to question and doubt—began to question things
that everyone else had been accepting as facts.

In that year of 1533, most of the accepted body of

"It's not right to cut up human flesh . . .!"

medical knowledge could be traced back to the research
of a Greek physician named Galen, who had lived almost 1,400 years earlier. Galen had based most of his
conclusions about human anatomy on his dissections
of monkeys and dogs.

Vesalius studied under the famous Professor Sylvius.
Like most scientists of his time, Sylvius accepted the
words of Galen as indisputable truth. And who dared
challenge Professor Sylvius!

No one—no one, that is, except Vesalius. His atti-
tude is summed up in a letter he wrote in those days
to a friend: "Everything is wrongly taught. Days are
wasted in absurd questions. And in the confusion, less
is offered to the student than a butcher in his stall
could teach a doctor."

The fame of his brilliance spread abroad, and soon
the University of Padua offered him a job as professor
of anatomy. Vesalius accepted, but on condition that
the university provide him with *human* bodies for dis-
section. The university agreed, convincing the city ad-
ministration that this would be a good way to dispose
of the bodies of criminals after execution.

Vesalius taught and worked at the university. His
painstaking studies yielded a wealth of information.
No one before him had ever sought out so thoroughly
the innermost secrets of the human body. Vesalius was
now ready to give this knowledge to the world.

And so he produced his masterpiece, *On the Fabric*

of the Human Body, a profusely illustrated text on anatomy. Under the superb supervision of Vesalius, the drawings were executed by a man named Calcar, a pupil of the famous artist Titian. Their collaboration produced drawings of such great skill that they still excite the admiration of artists and physicians alike. This great, authoritative volume appeared during the same year (1543) that Copernicus wrote his theory of how planets move. Thus, modern anatomy and modern astronomy were both born within just a few weeks of each other.

Doctors and students of the day were quick to realize the importance of the book. The clear and bold drawings showed them the body's vessels, bones, and muscles as they really are. The text corrected more than 200 errors which had been "embalmed" in the ancient texts on anatomy and were still honored by teachers like Sylvius.

The way had now been opened for great new medical advances. Doctors could better understand the sicknesses they treated in various parts of the body. Surgeons had a trustworthy guide to help them in their operations on the body. It was as though someone had, for the very first time, thought of actually traveling on a certain road before drawing a map of that road!

And all this happened before Vesalius had even reached the age of 30! But Andreas' old teacher Sylvius grew furious with this young upstart. The "facts" on

"You have committed heresy . . ."

which all his teaching had been based were now being overthrown. His reputation hung in the balance. He felt himself attacked, and resorted to accusation. "You have committed heresy," he cried. "You have blasphemed the memory of the great Galen."

Other doctors, equally jealous and bigoted, joined the hue and cry. "Vesalius is an impostor and a madman who, for sensationalism, proclaims error. He betrays Galen and all of us."

Vesalius was heartbroken, knowing that he was helpless against blind superstition and ignorance. Though some loyal students and colleagues stood by him, he was forced to resign from the university.

Vesalius spent the last 20 years of his life as royal physician to the court of Spain. His fame as a physician and surgeon spread around the world. He continued his studies of anatomy; but in Spain, too, since Church authorities disapproved of his use of human bodies, he developed powerful enemies.

Forced to flee Spain, he went to Jerusalem. And then came one of the great satisfactions of his life. The University of Padua asked him to return to his old job as professor. Influential scientists in Italy and France were beginning to accept his theories, after all.

Though Vesalius set sail for Italy, he never reached it. He was lost at sea in a shipwreck. But his work lives on in the enormous influence he had on medicine. Doctors revere him as the *Father of Modern Anatomy*.

GALILEO GALILEI

(1564-1642)

Founder of Experimental Science

IT TAKES great courage to stand up before people and say, "You are all wrong. I am right and I can prove it." Galileo risked his very life to do just that.

Galileo Galilei was born in 1564 in the ancient city of Pisa, Italy. When Galileo was a young man in his twenties, he was studying to be a doctor at the university. He kept noticing things. Certain ideas seemed unreasonable to him and he would protest and ask why they were taken for granted to be true. His teachers would get angry and tell him he was conceited.

"Who do you think you are to doubt the wisdom of all the great men who came before you?" they would say. But Galileo would not give in. He kept experimenting privately. One day, he obtained actual proof that what everyone believed to be true was not so.

The great Greek scholar, Aristotle, had said that a heavy object fell to earth faster than a lighter object. For 2,300 years people had taken this idea for granted. It seemed logical. But not to Galileo! His experiments proved to him that the notion was false. He announced he would give a public demonstration! He invited anyone and everyone to come and see for themselves.

Now in the town of Pisa where Galileo lived, there is a famous tower. On the appointed day, Galileo climbed this high tower, carrying with him two cannonballs. One weighed one pound; the other weighed ten pounds. While the crowd watched from below, Galileo dropped both balls from the top of the tower at exactly the same moment. The crowd gasped in astonishment. For just as Galileo had claimed, *both balls hit the ground at exactly the same moment!*

"Here is your proof," declared Galileo to the crowd assembled around the leaning tower. "Aristotle was wrong, as you have just seen with your own eyes. Objects fall at the same rate of speed!"

The old professors were so stunned and so angry that some of them claimed it was magic. But soon enough, since they saw that anyone could do the same thing, they had to admit Galileo's demonstration was not magic but a scientific fact.

Galileo became famous overnight. Now all his ideas were given a hearing. He believed, with the great Polish scientist, Copernicus, that the sun and the planets did not circle around the earth—that, on the contrary, the planets and the earth revolved about the sun. Fifty years earlier, few people had believed Copernicus. But now, because Galileo had become famous as a scientist, they began to consider that this, too, might be true.

Galileo always had an open mind. When he heard that some other scientist had developed a new theory, he investigated the claim and tried to find out for himself if it was true.

So it was that when he heard that a Dutchman named Hans Lippershay had developed a set of lenses that made it possible to see great distances, he, too, tried to make such an instrument. He improved this instrument—the telescope—so much that he came to discover great new facts about the universe.

With his telescope, Galileo was able to show that the sun itself whirled on its axis. He proved that the

. . . both balls hit the ground at the same moment.

moon was not a ball of smooth polished metal but that there were mountains on its surface. With his telescope, he discovered that the planet Jupiter had many moons of its own.

The whole world became excited by his discoveries. Kings and other prominent people came to his garden to look through his telescope and be thrilled at what they saw.

By this time, Galileo was held in great honor. He was given enough money so that he didn't have to worry about earning a living, but could spend all of his time studying and learning. But he had enemies who were jealous of him, who were always trying to discredit him. In his old age, they succeeded in turning the leaders of the Church against him.

Galileo had said again and again that the earth and all the planets revolved around the sun, that the earth was not the center of the whole universe. But his critics insisted such a belief contradicted the Bible, and that therefore Galileo was against religion. They had him brought up before a Church court on charges of heresy. This court threatened him with terrible punishment and possible death unless he admitted he was wrong.

It was a sad and heartbreaking sight to see this remarkable man forced to retract what he had spent his life proving. But today the whole world knows that Galileo was right, and respects him as one of the greatest scientists who ever lived.

JOHANNES KEPLER

(1571-1630)

Builder of Modern Astronomy

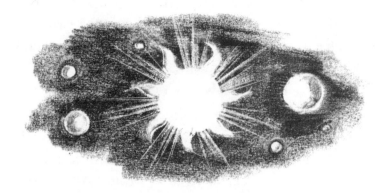

ALL HIS LIFE, overcoming handicaps was a constant
challenge to Johannes Kepler. At the age of four, a
disease crippled his hands and weakened his eyes. Illness, poverty, and family troubles were with him always. Yet he overcame them all to become one of the
greatest astronomers of all times!

Born in Germany in 1571, his brilliant mind got
him free early schooling, and later he won a university
scholarship. By the time he was 23, Kepler was made
Professor of Mathematics at Graz University.

Johannes spent his spare time studying astronomy,
and exchanged notes with two famous astronomers,
the Italian, Galileo, and Tycho Brahe, the Dane. Brahe
later invited Kepler to assist him at his observatory

near Prague. When Brahe died, he left Johannes his papers and instruments. With these valuable aids, Kepler could use his enormous mathematical knowledge to the utmost.

Succeeding Brahe as astronomer to Emperor Rudolph II of Bohemia, Kepler carried forward two projects. One was to prepare a set of tables that would accurately predict the positions of the planets. The other was to find the laws of motion governing the movements of the planets.

At that time many astronomers knew the earth turned on its axis. But they all believed that the planets moved around the sun in *circular* orbits. After more than six years of study, Kepler wrote a book, "The New Astronomy." He showed that Mars made an

Johannes spent his spare time studying astronomy . . .

elliptical, or oval, orbit at a speed varying according
to its distance from the sun.

This opened the way for his study of the other
planets, and he found that they also moved elliptically,
like Mars. The time they took to go around the sun
had an exact relation to their distance from it. Then,
from his findings, he drew up laws on planetary motion. Even today, these enable us to locate any planet
in its orbit at any particular time. They are the foundation of modern astronomy.

All knowledge is a growing thing. Like relay run-
ners, each great scientist passes on the stick of research
to the next one. Without Brahe's help, Kepler might
not have found his laws. Perhaps, without letters from
Galileo, he could not have used his mathematical
genius to its fullest.

Kepler passed along *his* stick of knowledge. From
his work grew the branch of mathematics called *cal-
culus.* Later, Newton used Johannes' laws to prove his
own universal law of gravitation. And Kepler handed
on a set of tables called "The Rudolphonic" which
were used for over a hundred years! Together with
other valuable information, these enabled geographers
and navigators to compute longitude.

Thus a poor, crippled boy who grew up to suffer
almost lifelong illness, refused to let hardships stop
him. He used his brain and evolved the laws which
are the basis of modern astronomy.

WILLIAM HARVEY

(1578-1657)

Founder of Modern Physiology

ON A YELLOWED marble wall, at the ancient University of Padua in Italy, there is still to be seen a tablet commemorating one of its most famous students—an Englishman by the name of William Harvey. Because it was the most renowned medical school of the time, good students from all over the world went to study at that seat of learning.

It was around the year 1600 when Fabricius, Professor of Anatomy at Padua and the beloved teacher of William Harvey, made the amazing discovery that veins are equipped with valves. He wondered, *What are they for?* And he asked his favorite pupil, "What do *you* think?"

William Harvey didn't know what to think, but he

was determined to find out. He returned to England, married, and set himself up in medical practice. He spent the next fourteen years dissecting animals, and cutting up the bodies of executed criminals. He experimented, made observations, and collected data.

Doctors the world over had been collecting data. We call this body of verifiable or provable information *facts.* Science is the study of facts. Harvey was interested in the facts of physiology—that is, the functions of the body's organs.

When Harvey disclosed some of his ideas in a series of lectures at the Royal College of Physicians in London, most of the doctors considered his notions the result of too much foreign influence—particularly from those extravagant, wild Italians. Ignorance is a stubborn enemy, and new ideas are not readily accepted. Yet, there were a few colleagues and friends who listened. Fortunately, there are always a few forward-looking people who will listen.

Harvey's fame spread—eventually, as far as King Charles I of England. Here Harvey found a friend!

King Charles believed in the *Divine Right of Kings,* and in keeping with this belief, he held that all knowledge was the province of the monarch. The King summoned Harvey to Whitehall. That afternoon, the King heard about one of the greatest discoveries concerning the human body—the theory of the circulation of the blood.

"Your Majesty," Harvey said simply, "the heart is a pump!"

"A pump, sir? I don't understand you," the King answered.

'You may have noticed, Sire," Harvey started to explain, "the spurting effect when an artery is severed?"

"I have watched criminals beheaded," the King answered. "It is an extremely bloody way to die!"

Harvey continued his explanation. "About seventy times a minute, one-fourth of an ounce of blood is expelled from the heart. At seventy beats a minute, nearly twenty pounds of blood should be expelled during an hour. I drained every drop of blood from the body of a sheep. The animal had only *four pounds* of blood in him altogether."

"How extraordinary!" exclaimed the King.

"Not at all, Sire. It had to be *the same blood* that was being pumped over and over again. The blood performs a circuit."

"That sounds logical," the King replied, "but how and where does it go, and what does it do?"

"The heart," Harvey answered, 'is a powerful hollow muscle divided into two main chambers called the *ventricles.* When the heart contracts, every second or oftener, blood is squeezed from these chambers into the pipes of the *arteries* leading from them. Between each ventricle and its artery, there is a valve. This valve opens away from the ventricle so that when the chamber starts to expand again, the blood will not flow back into it."

"I am not a physician, Mr. Harvey," the King said, in his usual polite way. "Can you say it more simply?"

"Indeed, Sire. The blood flows from the heart to every part of the body; carries away with it impurities from the body; comes back once again to the heart; and then flows into the lungs to purify itself. Then, after passing through the lungs, it comes back to the heart, making a complete circuit."

"You have convinced me," the King said. He made Harvey his personal attending physician, and permitted him to carry on further studies by observing animals in the royal deer park.

Harvey published his findings in 1628. But he caught the world unprepared. Men could not grasp this theory that broke so completely with tradition. It was foolish, indeed, to claim that blood moved in a circle; but to insist that it was the *same* blood, used over and over again—this was an offense against God and Nature. Surely, any sane man could understand that a body would sicken if the same old impure blood were pumped through it again and again. A historian of the time wrote: "'Twas believed by the vulgar that he was crack-brained, and the physicians were against him."

The King, however, had confidence, and Harvey continued to find favor at Court. But his colleagues, in-

"Your Majesty . . . the heart is a pump!"

tensely jealous of him, found a way to injure him.

There came a time when the King led his Royalist Party in battle against the opposing Parliamentarians. At the Battle of Edgehill, while the Royal Physician was attending the King, Harvey's enemies ransacked his house, took all his furniture, and maliciously destroyed and despoiled the contents of his museum, with all his specimens, his notes, and his experiments.

After the defeat of the Royalists and the execution of King Charles—who, unknowingly, had earlier described his own bloody death by beheading—Harvey retired to Oxford. There he continued his studies until his death at the age of eighty.

Though largely unappreciated during his lifetime, Harvey's discoveries of the function of the heart and of the circulation of the blood upset all theories held at the time, and laid the basis for modern medical knowledge.

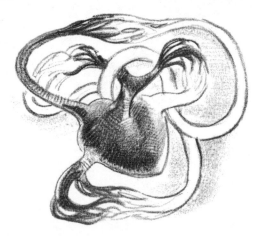

ANTONY VAN LEEUWENHOEK

(1632-1723)

Father of Microbiology

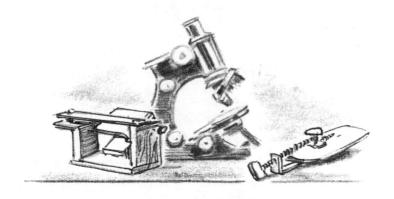

"HE'S CRAZY, I tell you," said a burgher of Delft to his friend one day, "crazy as a loon. That Antony never stops peering through those silly pieces of glass."

"Yes," replied his friend. "He would do better if he spent more time cleaning the City Hall. After all, he's just a janitor!"

"Why, do you know what he asked me for yesterday?" said the town butcher, who had joined the two men. "The eye of an ox! Oh, he's not going to eat it! He wants to study the eye with those lenses he's always grinding."

All the townspeople of Delft were talking about the queer janitor. Each day after finishing his work, Antony van Leeuwenhoek would rush back to his house among the canals and windmills. He would shut himself up for hours on end. He would squint through tiny lenses—lenses which he had spent long days and weeks grinding to perfection. What did he see through these lenses, lenses which he called by such a strange name— microscopes?

When Leeuwenhoek was a boy, there were no microscopes. The best the spectaclemakers of the time could do was to grind out a poor kind of magnifying glass. But young Antony thought it was wonderful that a simple piece of glass could make things look bigger—even a *little* bigger. "Suppose I were ever so careful and worked ever so hard. Perhaps I could make lenses so good that even the tiniest things would become large," Antony thought.

Almost every day, Leeuwenhoek watched the spectaclemakers grinding their lenses. When he learned all he could from them, he began to work at home by himself. How many times he must have been discouraged! How many lenses must have been ruined after weeks of labor! But Leeuwenhoek was stubborn. He would make *better* lenses no matter *how* long it took!

At last, his hard work was rewarded. His lenses were powerful. Although no one knew it at the time, the persistent janitor had made the best lenses not only in Holland—but in the whole wide world! Compared to our modern complicated instruments, his lenses were simple and crude. But crude or not, they made things 270 times bigger than life.

Antony van Leeuwenhoek's miraculous bits of glass were called microscopes—a name derived from the Greek words *micro,* meaning small, and *scope,* to see.

For Antony, one microscope was not enough. The tireless Leeuwenhoek made hundreds. Each microscope was to become a window opening on a mysterious world no one had ever dreamed existed. Let the foolish people of Delft make fun of him! He lived in a world of his own—a world peopled by his lenses and what he could see through them. There were not enough hours in each day for his observations. Late at night, a feeble candlelight flickered in his laboratory window. Passers-by saw Leeuwenhoek bent over his microscopes, muttering to himself.

Nothing was too weird for this curious and painstaking man. When he was not examining a fly's head, he was looking at the muscles of a whale, or at spiderwebs, or at plant seeds, or at his own skin. He even pulled hairs from a friend's mustache and put them under his lens!

What wonders he saw! Everything became transformed as if by magic. The fly's head, which was so tiny to the naked eye, became huge and intricate under his glass. And his friend could not believe that the thick, rough branch he saw through the microscope was really a hair from his mustache.

Leeuwenhoek pored over these marvels every day, alone. For in those days he lived a secluded life. He had no one to confide in. It is true that some curious friend or neighbor might come by for a peek through a lens. But his acquaintances were almost all uncultured people, as was Leeuwenhoek himself. The janitor of Delft could not even write Latin, which at that time was the language of scholars throughout Europe.

It never entered Antony's mind that scientists would be interested in what he observed through his microscopes. Why would such highly educated men pay attention to such a simple fellow as himself? He loved his lenses for what they could show him. He cared nothing about becoming rich or famous.

But one fine day Leeuwenhoek had a distinguished visitor. He was the respected Dutch scientist, Regnier de Graaf. De Graaf had heard many unbelievable tales about what Leeuwenhoek could see with his lenses. The scientist finally had come to find out for himself if these stories were true.

What De Graaf saw made him rub his eyes. "Can such things be possible!" he cried. "Leeuwenhoek, you should not keep all this to yourself. You must write to the Royal Society in England. The members are great and brilliant. They will welcome a description of what your microscopes reveal."

Soon after, there began an exchange of letters between the Dutch janitor and the prominent members

Passers-by saw Leeuwenhoek bent over his microscopes.

of the Royal Society. This correspondence continued
uninterrupted for fifty years—as long as Leeuwenhoek
lived.

What did he write in his long and rambling letters?
Some of the most astounding things in the history of
science. For these letters almost always told about fantastic discoveries.

His most amazing discovery was not to come until
one September day in 1675. The autumn rains had
begun. Leeuwenhoek thought it would be a good time
to see what rain water looked like under his microscope. He collected some water from a bowl he had
left in his garden. With his usual care, he put a tiny
drop of rain water under his lens. Then he squinted
down at it. And even Leeuwenhoek was not prepared
for what met his eye.

"Animals!" he cried. "Tiny animals! They're moving . . . and spinning around. They must be alive!
Yet so small . . . beside them, a flea would look as
huge as an elephant."

Leeuwenhoek peered for hours at the tiny creatures
living in the rain water. Did his eyes betray him? He
had spent years training his powers of observation. He
never accepted anything until he checked and rechecked
his observations. This time he must be doubly careful.
Only after long deliberation did he finally decide to
write to the Royal Society.

What a discovery! Leeuwenhoek himself had no

idea of its importance. He had discovered a new world. The janitor of Delft had found a kingdom in a drop of rain water. His universe was inhabited by animals too small to be seen with the human eye.

"Animals ten thousand times smaller than a water flea? The man's gone out of his head!" exclaimed an eminent member of the Royal Society.

Leeuwenhoek's letter describing his tiny animals, "wretched animalcules" he called them, had arrived in London. Most of the distinguished members did not know whether to laugh or be angry at the wild Dutchman writing such foolishness. No reasonable man could imagine animals so small that thousands could exist in a drop of water!

But a few members spoke up in defense of the janitor of Delft. Hadn't he always written them the truth? Perhaps it would be better to see for themselves—to repeat Leeuwenhoek's experiment, here in England.

And then—when the English scientists crowded around their microscope, when they actually saw the tiny animals with their own eyes, they knew that science had achieved one of its momentous discoveries. Years later, scientists realized that Leeuwenhoek's "wretched animalcules" were one-celled animals: the first living things believed to have existed on earth.

For Leeuwenhoek, vindication was but a meager prize. He set himself new goals, and discovery was to follow discovery. He was a never-tiring explorer. Even the mouths of his neighbors were not safe. He scraped between their teeth and found a certain "stuff" which was to prove even more important than the one-celled animals.

His microscope disclosed strange new beings making their home in the "stuff" from his neighbors' mouths. Some of these strange creatures were long and thin! Others were bent in the middle. Still others were spiral-shaped and spun around like tops. Leeuwenhoek found their actions hard to understand, but he reported his findings to the Royal Society.

Two hundred years later, the French scientist, Pas-

*. . the Queen of England came to look through
Leeuwenhoek's pieces of glass.*

teur, would identify these "strange new creatures" as
bacteria—the smallest plants on earth. Many of these
tiny plants are far more dangerous than the hungriest
lions or tigers. For bacteria have caused our worst
diseases and killed more people than all the wars in
history.

Then Leeuwenhoek turned his attention to one of
Nature's greatest mysteries—the blood. He was to be
the first to solve a riddle that had puzzled the most
brilliant minds of his day.

When the famous English surgeon, Dr. Harvey,
found how the blood circulates through the body, there
were those who still expressed their doubts. "How does
the blood get from the arteries to the veins?" the
doubters asked.

Harvey replied that the blood passed through vessels so small that they were invisible to the eye.
"Where is your proof?" the doctors scoffed.

It was Leeuwenhoek who provided the proof. He
was studying the transparent tail of a tadpole one day,
searching for the tiny blood vessels Harvey had described. No one had ever seen blood vessels before.
But through his microscope, Leeuwenhoek saw red
blood cells for the first time. He was entranced to see
the red cells narrow down until they were thin enough
to slip through the tiny tubes in their voyage from
the arteries to the veins. Harvey's theory was proven
correct.

The janitor of Delft grew older. And with the passing of the years, his passion for his microscopic world became ever greater. His name and his work became known among the scholars of all Europe. Honors were showered on him.

The simple Dutch townsman was elected a full member of the illustrious Royal Society. The equally distinguished French Academy of Sciences asked him to do it the honor of corresponding with its members. He received letters and congratulations from the most famous scientists and philosophers of the civilized world.

Imagine how the people of Delft felt when their janitor—whom some had called crazy—received a visit from Peter the Great, Czar of Russia! What could they say when the Queen of England came to look through Leeuwenhoek's silly pieces of glass?

Antony van Leeuwenhoek lived to be a very, very old man. But he remained healthy, and so dedicated to his life's work that he continued his observations until he was almost 90 years of age. When he was 91 years old, as he lay dying, he called his friend, Hoogvliet, to his side. "Hoogvliet," he whispered in a weak voice, "be so good as to send those two letters on the table . . . to London, to the Royal Society." In his last thoughts he remained as steadfast in his loyalty to science as he had been for half a century.

ISAAC NEWTON
(1642-1727)
Explorer of the Cosmos

YOUNG Isaac Newton sat peacefully dozing in the garden of his modest home. The sun was warm and the grass of the English countryside lay like a rich green carpet under his feet. How pleasant it was to forget the terrible plague which had ravaged London and forced the university at Cambridge to close!

The young student was half asleep. He could smell the sweet odor of the apples of the tree under which he was seated. Suddenly, Isaac's reverie was shattered.

Kerplunk! A ripe red apple fell squarely on young Newton's pate. He awoke with a start and rubbed his head for a moment. Then he picked up the apple which had struck him.

Anyone else would have been angry, or would perhaps have laughed about the apple's good aim. But not this 23-year-old fellow with a thirst for knowledge.

"Why," he asked himself as he examined the apple, "does the apple fall down? Why doesn't it fall up instead? I know the earth has an attraction for things and that its attraction is called gravity. But why, no matter how high a thing is, does it still fall to the ground?"

Then Isaac's mind took a leap into the unknown —where no scientist had ever ventured.

"This great attraction of the earth, which demonstrates its force to men who walk on its surface, likewise demonstrates its force through an apple that falls from *above* its surface. In similar fashion, gravity demonstrates its force through any falling object hurled from the top of a building *higher* than an apple tree. This great attraction of the earth—could it possibly reach *far out into the heavens?* Could it possibly reach up to the moon? If so, then the moon is subject to the same laws of gravity that made the apple fall.

"Perhaps the only thing that keeps the moon from flying wildly off into space and keeps it turning around the earth in an orderly, predictable fashion is this great force of gravity!

"And if the moon can be proved to be governed by gravity? Then the planets, the stars—even the universe itself—may be bound together by this force!"

Young Isaac's imagination had been set aflame. He

*"Why . . . does the apple fall down? Why doesn't it
fall up instead?"*

devoted much of his life to determining the laws which rule the universe. He became one of the greatest minds of the ages—a universal genius contributing to the sciences of physics, mathematics, astronomy, mechanics, and optics.

But Newton's fame rests chiefly on his discovery of the laws of gravity, laws which he formulated and which proved that the most immense planet hurtling through space obeys the same rules as a simple little apple falling from a tree. He discovered that "every object attracts every other object—according to their relative sizes and the distance between them."

Isaac Newton had solved one of the great riddles of the universe. And it all began with an apple.

ANTOINE LAVOISIER

(1743-1794)

Founder of Modern Chemistry

IT WAS THE YEAR 1794, the time of the Reign of Terror in Paris—a time when fear stalked the streets, a time of hysterical mob rule, a time of the supremacy of bloody vengeance. The peasant uprising against the King of France had already been successful; the French Revolution was an accomplished fact. But it was to be a long time before France settled down to an orderly process of democratic government.

Starving men, women, and children roamed the streets searching for bread and crying for revenge against their former oppressors. The leaders of the Revolution had become drunk with power, almost forgetting why they had fought against the tyranny of the crown. They could not give the people bread—so they gave them blood. There were daily public executions in which members of the nobility—some truly guilty of crimes against the people, others quite innocent— were beheaded. And as the sharp blade of the guillotine descended and lopped off a head, the mob would scream for more.

So it was that the guillotine claimed the life of one of the great scientists of all time—a man who had lived only to help others, who had devoted his life to the advancement of science and the betterment of mankind. Antoine Laurent Lavoisier had had the misfortune to be born wealthy.

When the soldiers came to his home to arrest him, Lavoisier was fully prepared to accept his fate, knowing the folly of fighting against blind ignorance and hysterical hatred. But his wife argued with the soldiers. "Why do you arrest my husband? He has always been on the side of the people. When the Revolution swept over France and defeated the King, he was overjoyed; he sang the *Marseillaise* with the crowds. He has worked for the Republic ever since. Even now, he is Director of your Academy of Science. There is not a truer lover of France than the man who stands before you."

The soldiers would not be moved. The leader spoke: "Madame, we have our orders. Monsieur Lavoisier has been accused of being a traitor to the Republic. He will be given a trial, and there he will have his chance to

The soldiers led Lavoisier to prison.

defend himself." The leader turned to Lavoisier and said, "Will you come with us peacefully, Monsieur, or must we take you by force?"

The soldiers led Lavoisier to prison. As he walked through the streets of his beloved Paris, he knew he would never walk them again as a free man.

Lavoisier waited in the "Prison of the Condemned" to go through what he knew would be a mere formality of a trial. Then, death. He did not lose his courage. He wrote to a cousin: "I have lived a reasonably long and happy life. I shall be spared the inconvenience of an old age, and I shall leave behind me a little knowledge and perhaps a little glory. What more can anyone expect in this world?"

Outraged messages poured in from leading scientists and statesmen all over Europe, protesting the brutal treatment of this world-famous scientist. But the Revolutionists were unyielding. The day of the trial arrived. Public interest had been aroused to a fever pitch. The courtroom was crowded with excited citizens.

The prosecutor bellowed: "I accuse Monsieur Antoine Laurent Lavoisier of plotting with foreign nations and the enemies of France."

Lavoisier's advocate asked, "And on what grounds, Sir, do you base your accusation? What evidence can you show the court?"

"I need no evidence," replied the prosecutor. "It is

well known that this man has engaged in mysterious scientific experiments with Englishmen, and with others who are enemies of our glorious new Republic."

The advocate could scarcely believe his ears. "What rubbish!" he exclaimed. "This is the talk of fools. Why, Monsieur Lavoisier has contributed more to the science of chemistry than any other man in the world today. He has written a book on the subject—*An Elementary Treatise of Chemistry*—that is universally recognized as the most complete and authoritative text in the field. Is this how we honor a man who has brought glory to France? Can he help it if ignorance forbids people to listen to the truths he expounds? I call on Monsieur Lavoisier to take the stand and explain to us some of his scientific discoveries."

Murmurs, and then shouts, swept through the crowd. An old hag, thin and pale from lack of food, screamed, "Off with his head! We don't need to hear any scientific nonsense!" A more intelligent voice was heard: "Monsieur Lavoisier deserves the right to speak in his own defense." The judge rapped for order and said, "You may proceed, Monsieur."

Lavoisier stood proud and unafraid, an impressive figure. He began to speak:

"For a long time, it was believed that a piece of wood burned because it contained 'fire-particles' —and that, as it burned, these fire-particles rushed out to form the ashes. We were told that only substances contain-

"Off with his head!"

ing these fire-particles would burn. Yet no one knew what the fire-particles were, and no one could prove that they actually existed. I conducted a careful experiment, burning tin in a sealed vase. I found that the remaining ashes weighed *more* than the original tin itself, yet the jar and its contents still weighed the same. I decided that if the fire-particles had burned, then the ashes *would have weighed less.* I then concluded that the air must have given something to the burning tin, something that added weight to the ashes. And it seemed that this gas from the air must be the cause of *combustion,* or burning.

"Then I found that when I burned sulphur, an acid was produced. I decided to call this gas from the air *oxygen,* meaning acid-former. Later, I found that water is not the pure, clear substance we think it to be, but that it is composed of this oxygen plus another gas, *hydrogen,* meaning water-former. These two gases, first identified by me, are now highly important elements in new experiments being performed by chemists. I, myself, am at present working on an experiment regarding the use the body makes of the oxygen it takes from the air. I believe that this oxygen we inhale is what starts heat in the body and keeps life going, but . . ."

The prosecutor interrupted him abruptly. "Enough, enough! We have listened patiently to all your learned spouting. But what have you proved? The plain fact remains that for many years you were a Farmer-General, a tax collector for the King. You squeezed money from the poor like blood from a turnip. You and your kind are what made life so miserable for all of us. We have no room left for you in the free, democratic Republic of France!"

And the crowd, easily inflamed by his emotional appeal, shouted angry denunciations—epithets aimed at every man who had ever collected the hard-earned money of the poor for taxes. But of course, all the abuse fell on the lone head of Antoine Lavoisier.

It was true that Lavoisier had been a tax collector, but he had taken this post to earn money needed for his scientific research. And he had always been scrupulously fair and honest with the peasants, often giving his own money to the poor rather than gouge them for heavy taxes.

The advocate tried to explain this to the angry crowd. "Many of you must know about the hundreds of deeds of kindness performed by this man. He never took money from those who needed it. His life was a model of Christian charity. Is this your reward to the noblest of men? How many of you have heard of the model farm that Monsieur Lavoisier started in the community of Blois, at his own expense? He taught the farmers new scientific methods of agriculture, and brought a new prosperity to the region. Even the great American revolutionary fighter, George Washington, hailed his achievements. The great American scientist and statesman, Benjamin Franklin, is a treasured friend of his. What better testimony do you ask to his honor and love of freedom? I say that France's name will be forever blackened if you do this ugly deed—if you take the life of this man."

It was an impassioned plea, but it was not heard. Antoine Lavoisier was convicted of treason and sentenced to death at the guillotine. Lavoisier was perhaps the only man present who was not moved by the prospect of his death. But he did have one request.

He addressed the judge: "Sir, I shall not argue over my sentence. God alone will pass judgment on my innocence. However, I beg of you simply to delay my execution for two weeks—give me just this short space of time in which to complete my experiment. The result may mean much more than my life or yours—for the advancement of science."

And the judge's amazing reply was: "The Revolution has no need of scientists; it needs justice."

So Lavoisier, the *Founder of Modern Chemistry,* went to his death. As a friend of his bitterly remarked, "It required but a moment to cut off his head; it may be another hundred years before the world sees another like it."

ALESSANDRO VOLTA

(1745-1827)

Inventor of the First Electric Battery

WHEN YOU SEE a sign marked *Danger—High Voltage,* or hear someone say, "This flashlight battery has one and one-half volts," do you know that a great scientist, Count Alessandro Volta, is being honored?

Count Volta lived about 200 years ago, in Italy. He heard about Dr. Galvani's celebrated experiment of the jumping frogs. Dr. Galvani knew how to set up the experiment which made dead frogs jump, but he did not know *why* they jumped.

It was Volta who was first to find the scientific reason for it. He discovered that when you place something moist between two different metals (Galvani had placed a wet frog between copper and iron), a current results.

. . . he generated enough electrical current . . . to
make a dead frog's legs kick . . .

Count Volta piled up round pieces of silver and zinc, the way we sometimes build a pile of checkers. Separating each disc from the next was a piece of heavy paper which had been soaked in salt water. Then he attached a wire to each end of the pile. With this pile he generated enough electrical current not only to make a dead frog's legs kick, but to give an electrical shock to anyone who held the wires.

This experiment is famous. It is know as the *Voltaic Pile*. It is also called the *Galvanic Pile*, for it was developed as a result of Galvani's experiments. But the word *volt*, which describes an exact measure of electrical pressure, is used all over the world. Thus, the honored name of Alessandro Volta lives on.

CHARLES GOODYEAR

(1800-1860)

Founder of the Rubber Industry

MRS. GOODYEAR was bustling around her crude little kitchen. It was time to prepare dinner for her husband, Charles, and their seven children. But she faced serious problems.

For one thing, there just wasn't any food in the house. "Oh, dear, will I have to go borrow from the neighbors again?" she thought. The Goodyears were very poor. Their life for the past few years had been a hand-to-mouth struggle.

Worse still, if Mrs. Goodyear did manage to get food, she would have a hard time finding something to cook it in. Her pots, pans, and oven were all full of rubber. That's right—rubber!

Charles Goodyear was known as "The Rubber

Maniac" to people around Boston. If someone asked to be directed to Mr. Goodyear, the usual reply was: "If you see a man with an India-rubber coat on, India-rubber shoes on, and an India-rubber cap on, and with an India-rubber purse in his pocket with not a cent in it—that is Charles Goodyear."

India-rubber had been introduced into the United States in 1832 with short-lived success. Its flexibility made it suitable for many uses. But it had one serious shortcoming: it melted into a sticky mess in the summer and froze hard during the winter.

Goodyear, a young hardware salesman, was convinced he could find a way to overcome these difficulties. He had had no formal training in chemistry. Yet he worked for five long years, trying just about everything that came into his imaginative mind. And though his experiments filled his whole house with rubber, Mrs. Goodyear had faith in her husband and did not complain.

They had borrowed money wherever they could; and somehow they had managed to scrape by. Several times, Charles had gone to jail because he couldn't pay his debts. But he was so persistent that he even continued his experimenting inside jail.

By that time, he had developed half of the process that was to make his name famous. By adding sulphur to the rubber and drying the substance in the sun, he found that its resistance to heat and cold was greatly

improved. But the rubber was still far from being a commercially usable product.

Then one of those once-in-a-lifetime lucky accidents happened—the kind inventors dream of! One evening, Goodyear was entertaining a few friends in his home. As usual, he was showing them pieces of rubber he had worked on—explaining the problems and how he hoped to solve them. One of the men, while handing the rubber back to Goodyear, carelessly

"Look! The rubber isn't melting at all."

dropped some of the material on the hot stove. "Sorry, Charlie," he said. "Here, I'll grab it before you have a sticky mess all over the stove."

But Goodyear yelled, "No, wait! Look! The rubber isn't melting at all. The heat is charring it, but one spot looks perfectly cured."

Goodyear had found his answer. *Heat* would take care of the defect in his rubber.

The next step would be to test the rubber at various degrees of heat, until the exact temperature was reached to yield the best result.

There followed five more years of careful experimenting until Goodyear had perfected the process. This process came to be known as *vulcanization*.

At last, Charles Goodyear fulfilled his life-long dream. It didn't take long for the world to realize that hundreds of products could be made with this marvelous substance. This new rubber had the invaluable properties of strength, durability, and elasticity.

The last years of Goodyear's life were happy years. No longer did his family live in poverty. Single-handedly, this man had founded a vast new industry, given employment to thousands of people, made life more comfortable, convenient, healthier.

Today, it's hard to imagine a world without rubber. From rubber bands to automobile tires—the world is indebted to Charles Goodyear.

MICHAEL FARADAY

(1791-1867)

Pioneer in Electricity

MICHAEL FARADAY was the son of a poor London blacksmith. His parents and other relatives were good, honest, plain people with no particular talents. Michael had very little schooling, and was not an outstanding student. Yet Michael Faraday was destined to contribute more to the development of the theory of electricity than any other man in the history of science. He became the *Pioneer of the Electrical Age.*

Young Faraday had always been fascinated by electricity. Perhaps it all began when he was a small child, huddled on the floor of his family's miserable little one-room hovel. He would watch his father, the blacksmith, pounding white-hot iron. And Michael's

eyes would glow, lit up by the sparks that flew from
his father's anvil. Hunger, cold, ragged clothes—all
were forgotten in the magic of that spectacle.

Michael's boyhood was a short one indeed. At the
age of thirteen, he was sent out to earn his own living and help contribute to his family's pitifully small
income. It was not that his father was mean to him,
but simply that there was not enough bread to go
around. And in those days, many a boy went to work
at a much earlier age.

Michael was fortunate in the job he found. He became apprenticed to a bookseller. At first, he was
merely a delivery boy. But his energy, diligence, and
pleasing manners were soon noticed, and the bookseller began to teach Michael the craft of bookbinding.
As Michael toiled away with heavy treatises on history, science, philosophy, and religion, he also read
as much in these books as he could. His was a great
thirst for knowledge—especially for *scientific* knowledge—and that little bookshop was his university.

One day, a fine gentleman came into the shop with
a great set of encyclopedias, which were given to
Michael to be bound. Here was all the knowledge
of the world, waiting to be explored. Michael was fascinated. He devoured the sections on science, especially
the articles dealing with electricity.

Soon Michael began to spend part of his tiny salary
to attend the public lectures on science held in London.

One day, as he was leaving one of these lectures, he chanced to meet the owner of the encyclopedias.

"Good evening, Mr. Williams," he said politely.

"Why, what brings you here, lad?" the astonished gentleman asked.

"I came to hear the lecture on the subject of Sir Humphrey Davy's experiments with electricity, Sir," the boy replied.

"Well, bless my soul, you *are* an inquisitive one, aren't you? Tell me, my lad, how would you like to hear Sir Humphrey himself deliver a series of lectures?"

"Nothing would please me more, Sir," Michael replied. "But the cost of the tickets is far beyond my means."

Mr. Williams was quite impressed. "Here, take my tickets," he said. "I have a feeling that you will be able to make much better use of them than I ever could. But I'd like you to do me a favor. Will you come around afterwards, and tell me what Sir Humphrey had to say?"

The kindness of the old gentleman proved to be the turning point in Michael's career. Sir Humphrey Davy was the most brilliant scientist in England; his many discoveries had won him world-wide fame. Yet his discovery of Michael Faraday was to be, perhaps, his greatest contribution to the cause of science.

Michael attended the lectures fully equipped with notebooks and pencils. He took down detailed notes of everything the great man said. Then he went home, carefully wrote out reports of the lectures, and made illustrative diagrams. And then, because he wanted to make sure that he had really understood the lectures, he sent off his reports to the scientist, respectfully asking that Sir Humphrey correct any errors.

When Sir Humphrey examined young Faraday's reports, he was stunned. "This lad has a genius that deserves attention," he thought. "He is obviously self-taught. Though he still has much to learn, he has a brilliant comprehension of complex scientific theories. It's not so long since I, too, was a struggling young scientist. I *must* help him."

Michael was appointed by Davy as his laboratory assistant. It was a dream come true—to work closely

*One day a fine gentleman came into the shop with a
great set of encyclopedias . . .*

with such a great scientist. Though at first he did little more than wash bottles, sweep floors, and serve as handy man, he was able to observe and learn much. Here was a training ground that was far superior to any university he might attend.

When Sir Humphrey went on an extensive lecture tour of Europe, he took the boy along as his personal secretary and assistant. Michael met the finest scientists on the Continent, talked about problems, discussed various experiments. His mind was filled with hundreds of questions to which he wanted to find answers. Now he had the background that would enable him to begin an independent career in research.

During the following years, Faraday wrote scientific papers and delivered lectures. Gradually, he came to be recognized as a leading new voice in science. At the age of thirty-two, he was made a Fellow of the Royal Society, and the following year he lectured before that distinguished group. His services as an expert chemist were in great demand, and he was earning more money than he had ever dreamed of. But these activities left him little time for the research in pure science that was his consuming interest. So he gave up all consulting work, declined a professorship at the University of London, and accepted a small salary from the Royal Society that was enough to satisfy his modest needs and would leave him free to experiment as he pleased.

Faraday was vitally interested in the relationship between magnets and electricity. He knew that a magnet affected electricity, and that electricity affected a magnet—but how and why? It took long, hard work, and many disappointing experiments, before he had found his answers. But he finally discovered a way of making an electrically charged wire rotate around a magnet. This discovery by Faraday of the principle of *electro-magnetic induction* formed the basis for the development of all electrical theory that followed. Electric motors, which play such an important role in our life today, were a direct outcome of Faraday's experiments and discoveries. Some time later, he developed the principles on which electrical generators and transformers are based.

His wonderful accomplishments brought him fame and honor. But when it was proposed that he be made President of the Royal Society—the highest reward that the grateful English could bestow on their most brilliant scientist—he declined the offer. "I must remain plain Michael Faraday to the last," he said.

And plain Michael Faraday he remained. He lived quietly and happily in the cottage given him by Queen Victoria, continuing with his experiments and his lectures. Faraday died at the age of seventy-six, his life's work universally hailed as "a career of discovery unparalleled in the history of pure and experimental science."

WILLIAM MORTON
(1819-1868)
Crusader Against Pain

THE EVENING AIR was a bit chilly, even for late September in Boston. But Eben Frost, a mild-mannered music teacher, was concerned with more than the cold as he walked hesitantly along Tremont Row. Eben Frost had just one concern—one overwhelming concern that blocked out just about everything else. Eben Frost had a dreadful toothache!

He paused in front of Number 19, peering at the sign that read "William Morton, Surgeon-Dentist." His friends had told him, "If your tooth hurts, then you just go to Dr. Morton. He'll yank it out nicely for you." And when he had protested that having it pulled would hurt so much, they laughed. "And how do you expect to get rid of that tooth without some pain?"

That was in the year 1846, before anyone had discovered a successful pain-killer. All operations—from a tooth extraction to the amputation of a leg—were performed with the patient wide-awake and in agony.

Frost was terrified as he thought of what lay in store for him. He was ready to forget the whole thing and go back home, when suddenly a terrible pain shot through his jaw. He had to face up to the ordeal. Either suffer with this tooth for goodness knows how long, or endure the few awful minutes while it was being pulled.

His decision made, he climbed slowly up the narrow stairs. His feeble knock on the door was immediately answered by a man who almost seemed to expect him.

"I have a toothache," said Frost.

"Excellent," replied Dr. Morton, who set about getting his instruments ready.

Seated in the "torture" chair, poor Frost made one last attempt. "Doctor, I'm scared! Isn't there anything you can do to relieve the pain? M-m-maybe you could hypnotize me!"

The young doctor reassured him. "Now you just relax. I think I have something here that's much better than hypnotism. Open your mouth, please. Oh, that *is* a bad tooth."

Then Dr. Morton poured some liquid into a handkerchief, placed it over the patient's nose, and instructed him to inhale. Frost was aware of a sickly-sweet odor. Then everything began to fade into the distance. He could hear the dentist saying, "Breathe deeply . . ." Then he was asleep; and a smile appeared on his face for the first time that day.

When Frost awoke a few minutes later, Morton stood there with the ugly tooth in his hand. The patient couldn't believe his eyes. "I must be dreaming," he said. "I didn't feel a thing!" But then he tasted the blood in his mouth, and his tongue touched an empty space instead of an aching tooth. "It's a miracle, that's what it is! Hurrah!"

What seemed a miracle to Frost was the result of several years of hard work by William Morton. The dentist had watched *so* many patients suffer. He had become convinced that there must be a way of deadening the pain during an operation, without harming the patient in any way. Other doctors through the ages had tried alcohol, opium, "laughing gas," hypnotism, and thousands of crackpot schemes. Nothing really worked. When Morton found out about the unusual powers of a substance called *ether,* he thought he had the answer. Fate brought him Eben Frost as his first test case.

Morton's mind reeled as he thought of the future possibilities for ether. Pulling a tooth was one thing. But just suppose that surgeons could put patients to sleep while cutting off a leg or removing a diseased

"I have a toothache . . ."

growth from the body. Would ether blot out the pain in such serious operations as these?

News of Morton's discovery swept through Boston like wildfire. Many were skeptical. A 27-year-old dentist who was only a second-year medical student at Harvard—how could *he* succeed where so many wiser men had failed?

But Dr. Warren, a famous surgeon at Massachussetts General Hospital, decided to give the young man a chance. Warren was scheduled to remove a tumor from a patient's neck. He invited Morton to try out his pain-killer in this operation.

The operation was to begin at 10 o'clock in the morning. By that time, the hospital amphitheater was filled with excited students and doctors. The patient, Gilbert Abbott, lay on the operating table in full view. Dr. Warren was ready to begin.

Morton approached Abbott. "I'm going to give you something that will put you to sleep. You won't feel the knife at all. Are you willing to let me try?"

Abbott agreed. Like Frost, he would try anything that might shut out the pain. Soon he was fast asleep, dreaming of happier things than operations. A hush fell over the crowd as Dr. Warren skillfully cut away the tumor. Not a sound out of the patient.

As Abbott stirred into consciousness a few minutes later, Dr. Warren leaned over him anxiously. "Did you feel anything?" he asked.

Abbott was still smiling. "No . . . I seem to remember someone tickling my neck, but that's all. Thank God!"

Dr. Warren turned to face the amazed audience. They probably expected a high-sounding, scientific speech from him. But his five words are now historic: "Gentlemen, this is no humbug!" It was a moment of great triumph.

The story of the operation was published in a Boston medical journal. Oliver Wendell Holmes, the renowned writer, suggested a name for the new process—*anesthesia,* meaning "insensibility." Morton's fame spread, and doctors clamored for permission to use his pain-killer.

But the medical profession had a firm rule—no medicine could be given to a patient unless the doctor had full knowledge of its ingredients. At first, Morton tried to keep secret the fact that his miraculous liquid was simply ether. He wanted to get a U.S. patent on the discovery, so that he could at least earn money to pay for his research. He had already given up his dental practice, and he intended to spend his time studying the further uses and effects of ether.

The pressure on him was very strong. Unless he revealed his secret, mankind would have to wait a long time before benefiting from his discovery. At last, he announced that the substance was nothing more nor less than plain ether.

A storm of protest followed. A friend claimed that he had originally told Morton about ether. Another doctor had used "laughing gas" in the same way. Dr. Crawford W. Long, in Georgia, had used ether for tooth-pullings some four years earlier. Dozens of other doctors claimed credit for making the discovery before Morton. Yet the fact remained that it *was* William

"Gentlemen, this is no humbug!"

Morton who first realized the value of ether, and who first used ether publicly in an operation.

The controversy raged for years. Morton was heavily in debt; and though anesthesia was now widely practiced and brought relief to thousands of suffering patients, the world refused to recognize his great contribution.

When the Civil War broke out, Morton enlisted in the Medical Corps. It was probably the most satisfying period of his life, for he saw his discovery being used day after day to help soldiers in their pain.

Today, Dr. William Morton is given full credit for his great service to humanity. But when he died, poor and almost forgotten, only a few faithful friends did him honor. They had the following words inscribed on his tomb:

WILLIAM T. G. MORTON
INVENTOR AND REVEALER OF ANESTHETIC
INHALATION. BY WHOM PAIN IN SURGERY WAS
AVERTED AND ANNULLED. BEFORE WHOM
SURGERY WAS IN ALL TIMES AGONY. SINCE WHOM
SCIENCE HAS CONTROL OF PAIN

CHARLES DARWIN

(1809-1882)

Originator of the Theory of Evolution

THE COLD DECEMBER gale whipped across the harbor in Portsmouth, England. It was a bleak, blustery day in 1831, and hardly the proper weather for setting out on a two-year ocean voyage, as the *Beagle* was scheduled to do. The little ship was tossing back and forth in the choppy waters like a toy boat.

A fresh-faced young student stood watching the vessel with great misgivings. Why was he, a born land-lubber, going to set foot on this creaky craft? Why, indeed? Because it was his opportunity of a lifetime to study living plants and animals—to study *naturalism*.

The voyage of the *Beagle* was a government-sponsored venture to chart the coasts and islands of South

America, Australia, and New Zealand. And this young man was lucky enough to have been chosen as the group's naturalist. Here was an unlimited opportunity to observe life in unexplored regions!

So this gentle young scientist took up his bags and crossed the gangplank to the deck. The ship was rolling mightily, and it was all he could do to avoid getting sick that instant. He was amazed to see hard-bitten sailors going about their business of making the ship ready, with no care about weather or heaving, just as though it were a nice June morning. He stepped up to the grizzled old skipper and spoke. "Charles Darwin reporting for the voyage, Sir."

"Um-m-m" was just about all he could make out of Captain Fitzroy's reply. Then: "You look a little green around the gills, Darwin," he snorted.

"Yes, Sir . . . I mean, no, Sir," Charles stammered. Yes, he was *very* green, and all he wanted was to go below to his quarters and be left alone in his misery.

So began a voyage that stretched into five years. It was a voyage that not only wrecked Darwin's already feeble health—it actually changed men's fundamental ideas. For what Darwin saw and learned during those five years formed the basis for his revolutionary theory of evolution—a theory that forced scientists to change their whole way of thinking about the origin of species and the story of life on this planet.

Every moment of the sea voyage was agony for

Darwin. He was continually seasick and was never able to overcome this sickness. Yet he forced himself to keep a careful and detailed account of everything he saw. He studied his data and compared results. The days he spent on land were exciting ones for him. He described his first sight of Brazil in this way: "I felt a perfect hurricane of delight and astonishment . . . The form of the orange tree, the coconut, the palm, the mango, the tree fern, the banana, will remain clear and separate; but the thousand beauties which united these into one perfect scene must fade away. Yet they will leave, like a tale heard in childhood, a picture full of indistinct but most beautiful figures."

Darwin was amazed at the strange and exotic plants and animals he saw in the tropical jungles. He endured great hardships of rough travel through fierce, wild growth to get a closer look at everything. Bitten by bugs and insects, he ignored the pains. For Darwin was fascinated by the new and wonderful creations which unfolded before his hungry eyes. Here were plants and animals undreamt of.

Gradually, Darwin began to develop a theory that contradicted everything the world believed in. He could classify each plant, animal, and bird he had seen with its corresponding species on the mainland. Yet each of these creatures had some characteristics that were completely different from those of their counterparts and relatives. It was an accepted scientific fact—

and had been for centuries—that all species of life were fixed and unchangeable. But just suppose—just suppose—that when a species finds itself in new surroundings, it begins to develop *new* form, *new* color, *new*

qualities to fit itself best to these new surroundings. And suppose that, after a long time, it might even change gradually into an entirely new species! Would this process of *evolution* explain the origin of life on earth?

Charles Darwin was staggered by the enormity of

"Charles Darwin reporting for the voyage sir."

his concept. But he could not force himself to deny what his eyes had seen and what his mind told him. All great scientists reach a point in their lives when they must dare to question something everyone else has accepted as "gospel." Darwin knew it would take him many long years to build up the evidence to support his far-reaching theory before he could present these revolutionary ideas to the scientific world.

Darwin returned to England, married, and retired to his country home to raise a family of ten children and conduct his scientific research. Though he was in almost constant physical agony for the remaining forty years of his life, he refused to become an invalid.

Darwin spent more than twenty years doing the most exhausting kind of work. He had brought back with him from his voyage hundreds of samples of shells, rocks, plants, animal bones, and so on; he carefully classified all of these, constantly checking and rechecking his theory at each turn.

Finally, he was ready to unveil *evolution.* Then one fateful day, a letter arrived from an unknown young naturalist, Alfred Russel Wallace, from a tiny island in the Indian Ocean. Darwin was flabbergasted to read Wallace's paper on the *theory of evolution by natural selection!* It was an idea that Wallace had hit on quite by chance while he lay sick with a fever. He was now asking for Darwin's sponsorship of his idea before the scientific societies in England.

Darwin was heartsick. What should he do? His first impulse was to give full credit to Wallace, who, after all, had entrusted him with the idea. But he decided to call in his two closest friends—the geologist Lyell and the botanist Hooker—and ask their advice.

"You see, gentlemen," he said, "my dilemma is quite serious. This young man's theory is almost exactly the same as mine. It is a most astonishing coincidence—one that the world might never believe. And I will not have either Wallace or anyone else thinking that I behaved badly. I would far rather burn my whole book."

"Tell me, Charles, have you not devoted twenty years of your life to working out this theory?" asked Lyell.

"Yes, that is true," replied Darwin, "and young Wallace dashed it all off in six weeks. But it is quite possible that the theory may not be able to stand alone, without the careful body of evidence I have built up to support it."

"But what does that mean?" asked Hooker.

"Just this," said Darwin. "Our friend Lyell has told us that through long periods of geological time, the earth itself underwent many unusual and complete changes. I believe that *organic* life may have gone through the very same kinds of changes—that through a process of *natural selection* those creatures survived that were best fitted to live in their special environ-

Darwin was amazed at the strange and exotic plants and animals.

ments. For instance, a furry animal would have a better chance of surviving in a cold, snowy climate than one who was not equipped with this natural fur coat. These creatures passed on their special traits to their offspring; and in the constant fight for survival of the fittest, certain species of animal and plant life developed. In this manner, there gradually came into being the highest type of animal we know—man."

Lyell could not bear the thought that his good friend might lose the credit for his wonderful contribution, and he made a suggestion: "Why not allow Hooker and me to present this theory before the Linnaean Society as the joint work of Wallace and you? If you insist on honoring Wallace's part in the discovery, then this is the only logical compromise. It would be foolish indeed to ignore the important role you have played."

Darwin agreed to this, and the paper was read to the Society in 1858. When Wallace heard the news, he immediately announced to the world that he wanted to be known only as a "disciple of Darwin." But Darwin continued to give honor and credit to Wallace. The relationship between these two men is a shining example in the history of science—a notable exception to such instances of contention as the fight over Morton's claim to have developed anesthesia or the numerous attempts of lesser men to take credit for Isaac Newton's scientific discoveries.

In the following year, Darwin's book *The Origin of Species* was published. It represented a lifetime of study and thought, and presented his complete development of the theory of evolution, buttressed by a great mass of facts to support the theory.

The book caused a sensation. There were endless public denunciations of Darwin, on personal as well as scientific grounds. Much of the opposition was grounded in religious objections. Darwin was too gentle and kind a man to reply to any of the vicious attacks made on him personally, but he deeply resented the accusations that he had attempted to disprove the existence of God. He wrote in a letter to a friend: "I have never been an atheist. I may say that the impossibility of conceiving that this grand and wondrous universe, with our conscious selves, arose through chance seems to me the chief argument for the existence of God."

In the one hundred years since the appearance of his book, of course, there has been much further research in the field. The fact of evolution has long since been accepted, though the theory of natural selection no longer appears to be the complete answer to the story of life. Many mysteries remain. But Darwin's work opened up a door that can never again be closed.

When he died, Charles Darwin was buried in Westminster Abbey, England's traditional resting-place for her greatest heroes.

LOUIS PASTEUR

(1822-1895)

Father of Preventive Medicine

"I HAVE found tiny creatures in your wine—so small, you cannot see them without a microscope. *They* are the reason why your wines have become diseased," declared Louis Pasteur.

"Tiny creatures?" asked an incredulous vintner. "Tiny creatures? How is that possible? How can *they* spoil the wine? Where do your tiny creatures come from?"

"From the air!" Pasteur cried. "They come from the air! They are carried by the dust!"

The assembled vintners threw up their hands. They looked at each other in amazement. Then one of their group spoke up. "Our fathers tended their vineyards for fifty years, and our grandfathers before them for still another half-century. For thirty or more summers, we have seen the grapes grow. We have watched every detail of wine-making since we were small children. Never before have we been stricken by such a heavy blight of disease. We have kept our cellars clean. Everything has been carefully supervised. Neither rain, nor heat, nor sleep has kept us from watching our precious wine. We have cared for our wine as a father would care for his children. Yet, here we stand near ruination.

"So it's tiny beasts, you say, that come from the air! Tiny little beings we can't see that are eating up our substance, Professor Pasteur! Tiny creatures that are destroying the vintners of France! *Incroyable!* Incredible, monsieur, incredible!"

He turned and faced the other men who stood by, dejected.

Yet this Professor Pasteur had the reputation of turning up with the most amazing explanations for baffling things.

"If there are small creatures, Monsieur Pasteur— small creatures no eye can see—that are ruining our wine, what can we do about it?" they asked.

Pasteur leaned forward. "Gentlemen," he said, "there is a way!

"First of all, you must keep your rooms dust-free, so that the little criminals can't gain access to your wine vats. Then, you must heat the wine!

"Yes," he exclaimed to the astonished vintners, "you must heat it! It is heat that will kill the tiny microbes which turn your wine sour!"

The advice was followed. The wine was saved, and Pasteur had salvaged an industry.

But more! Pasteur had revolutionized man's thinking about disease! If these tiny beings—microbes—caused disease, then disease could be banished from the earth! But first a way must be found to destroy microbes!

Before Pasteur had a chance to work out his theory completely, he was catapulted into another emergency. Old Professor Dumas, the man who had been his teacher when he was a chemistry student, came to appeal to him on behalf of the silk industry of France. Silkworms were dying by the millions from a mysterious affliction: French silk growers were on the verge of ruin.

It was 1865 when Pasteur started his research on the silkworm. He almost never finished that task. For during that terrible epoch of his life, his father died, his two daughters passed away, and he himself, overcome by work and sorrow, collapsed. One of his legs became partially paralyzed, an affliction which he bore to his grave. Yet Pasteur fought through, and was finally able to demonstrate how microbes caused the particular disease that was ravishing the silkworm.

Some time later, the French poultry farmers ap-

. . . each of the twenty-five sheep . . . gamboled about.

pealed to the man who had saved the wine industry and the silk industry. A cholera epidemic had attacked their poultry. Everywhere, chickens were dying by the thousands. Pasteur was called on to help; and soon he identified the germ which caused the epidemic.

Pasteur asked himself why, if he could find the germ that caused the disease, couldn't he find a way to *prevent* the disease? Countless experiments and much research followed. Then came a day when he hit upon one of those inspirations that change the course of history. Some of the soup in which he had been keeping chicken cholera germs had been left standing. Pasteur decided to inject some of this fluid into healthy chickens.

Wonder of wonders! The chickens became sick, but they did not die! Pasteur summarized the facts: "The weeks-old weakened strain of microbes made the chickens a *little* sick—but not sick enough to kill them. Once they have had a slight case of the disease, they build up a resistance to it. Then they never can be mortally afflicted, because their blood is now able to combat the germs. By injecting these chickens with a weak potion of the disease-bearing fluid, they have been rendered immune!"

But if this were true of chickens, wouldn't it be true of all animals? Wouldn't it be true, too, for man?

To Pasteur's mind, the procedure was simple: Find the microbe, prepare a weakened strain containing the microbe—a vaccine—and this vaccine could be a shield against the disease-bearing microbe.

"Aha!" sneered the critics. "A very pretty theory indeed! He carries on a lot of newfangled experiments in his laboratory. He issues pronouncements, claiming wonders and miracles. But let him work out in the open! Let him *demonstrate* his crazy theories in public!

"The disease of anthrax is killing half the sheep

and cattle of France. If Pasteur can prepare a vaccine to save the wretched animals, let him demonstrate his power!"

Pasteur accepted the challenge. On May 2, 1881, in the town of Melun, before a crowd of farmers, veterinarians, doctors, and newspaper reporters, Pasteur and his assistants confronted the famous veterinary experts, Doctor Rossignol and Doctor Biot. There, too, were a number of other well-known scientists who had scoffed at his theories. Fifty sheep were provided. Pasteur and his assistants injected 25 of them with the anthrax vaccine. The other 25 animals were not touched.

Then all 50 of the sheep were injected with wicked amounts of the murderous anthrax germs. Rossignol, Biot, and the skeptical farmers watched the macabre spectacle. They expected to see 50 dead sheep. What a useless waste of livestock! And livestock now so precious in France!

Then followed triumph. For while each sheep not protected by the vaccine collapsed and expired, each of the 25 sheep protected by the Pasteur vaccine gamboled about, munched grass, and behaved just as if it had never been exposed to anthrax.

This magnificent demonstration silenced Pasteur's critics forever. The world of science now was marshalled to destroy those diseases which had been ravishing mankind from time immemorial.

Louis Pasteur had grown old. His friends were urg-

ing him to retire. But before him still lay his greatest
work. He must prove that humans, too, could be saved
by vaccines.

He embarked upon a long series of experiments and
finally announced that he had developed a vaccine
against the dread disease of rabies.

In the small Alsatian town of Meisengott, a mad
dog had run wild, and had terrorized the populace.
Before the beast was brought to bay, he had knocked
down a 9-year-old lad and bitten him several times.
The doctors had shaken their heads sadly and told the
wailing and grief-stricken mother that they could do
nothing for little Joseph Meister. "The bite of a mad
dog means death," they said. "There is no power on
earth to save him."

"No power on earth—unless it be Louis Pasteur!"
cried a young physician. "He has a trunkful of miracles! Off to Paris, my dear lady. Off to Paris with the
boy. Get him quickly to the Pasteur laboratory!"

With trembling hands, Pasteur inoculated Joseph
with his vaccine—a vaccine that had never before been
tried on a human being!

During the next few weeks, the worried scientist
paced the floor in great anxiety. His life's work was at
stake. He could not sleep, nor could he eat.

But little Joseph was gay and cheerful. After each
treatment, he kissed his "dear Monsieur Pasteur" who
looked at him so benignly from his deep, sunken eyes.

*"Off to Paris with the boy! Get him quickly to the
Pasteur laboratory!"*

When Joseph Meister recovered, the whole world was thrilled. Into Paris flocked the stricken from all corners of the earth. Among them were four American children. These four, too, were rescued from the very jaws of death by the wonder-working French scientist.

Now, from a grateful world, came contributions to construct the famous Pasteur Institute, where scientists still continue to search for new weapons against disease.

Pasteur's seventieth birthday was the occasion of a glorious celebration. World-famed scholars from many lands put aside their work to come and do him homage. The aged scientist, gray and bent, walked slowly to his seat, leaning on the arm of the President of the French Republic. Pasteur was too weak to read the speech which he had prepared, so his son read it for him. His words were directed to the young people of every nation.

"Live in the serene peace of laboratories and libraries," he told them. "Say to yourself, first of all, 'What have I done for my instruction?' And as you go on farther, ask yourselves, 'What have I done for my country?' until the time comes when you may have the happiness of thinking that you have contributed to the progress and welfare of humanity."

JOSEPH LISTER

(1827-1912)

Father of Modern Surgery

AFTER MORTON'S thrilling development of the use of anesthesia, there was a great increase in the number of operations performed, and the science of surgery flourished.

Let's visit a typical operating room in the year 1860. The doctors and attendants are gathered round the patient, who lies asleep on the table. The doctor's hands are *not* encased in rubber gloves. *No* masks cover the faces of the people in the room. The surgical instruments are *not* being washed in a sterilizing solution. And where is the white surgical gown we expect to see in an operating room? The surgeon is wearing an old black frock coat that seems to be covered with dirt and dried blood. And hanging from the lapel of this coat are the threads he will use to sew up the patient's wound!

Is this a particularly sloppy, badly run hospital? No, it is the famous Edinburgh Infirmary in Scotland, and the conditions are much the same as they are in other leading hospitals all over the world.

Surprisingly enough, only one man had begun to question such conditions. His name was Joseph Lister; and like other great trailblazers in science, he was considered a crackpot by his colleagues.

From his earliest days, Joseph Lister had been fascinated by surgery. After long years of study, he had become a skilled and successful surgeon. But he had

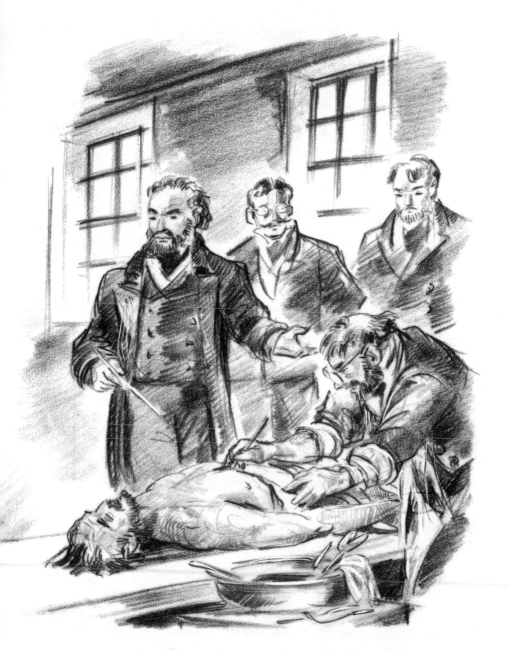

The surgeon is wearing an old black frock coat . . .

found that all his learning and all his skill in the use of the knife counted for little in the fierce battle against infection. No matter how well he performed an operation, he could usually expect the wound to swell, fester, and often result in death. This *suppuration* occurred after almost all operations. About four out of every ten people on whom operations were performed died soon afterward as a result of this "hospital disease." Other doctors accepted this development as the natural course of things, but Lister was greatly disturbed.

His father-in-law, the famous surgeon James Syme, told Lister, "Joseph, when you grow older and more experienced, you will become used to this. Death is an everyday fact with us. We do our best, but our power is limited."

And Joseph Lister answered: "I cannot believe this is true. I know that I take every care and precaution when I'm operating. And yet it *must* be that I and you and every other surgeon do something that causes this infection. I must find out what it is. I cannot go on killing people."

Though the unsanitary operating conditions of that time shock us, the possibility that germs might enter a wound and cause an infection was then quite unthought of.

However, Joseph Lister came very close to guessing this. After treating a number of patients with broken bones, he began to notice an interesting fact. Now, there are two kinds of *fractured,* or broken, bones—simple and compound. A simple fracture merely has to be set back in place and allowed to heal; Lister observed that these cases always recovered without the patient developing any other disease. But a compound fracture involves the penetration of the outside skin by the broken bone; in these cases, the patient usually developed an infection that led to amputation of the arm or leg, and death often followed.

Lister had a fantastic thought: "Suppose there is something in the air—something that enters these open wounds and causes the infection. That must be it! The body tissue doesn't just become diseased for no reason at all. We doctors allow another element to get inside the body. If I could only find out what it is, and then learn how to control it."

Lister's first step was to begin washing his hands *before* an operation as well as afterward. He also started to wear a clean white jacket while operating. Though he was on the right track, these few improvements made no noticeable difference in the over-all results. Just about all that happened was that the other doctors laughed at him: "What—a surgeon without his black frock-coat! Why, there's no telling what he'll think of next."

What Lister did think of next represented a historic advance. One night he was reading Pasteur's article describing experiments that the scientist had performed on wine fermentation. He was arrested by Pasteur's statement that tiny microbes had caused wine to turn sour.

Suddenly, he had a flash of inspiration. He jumped out of his chair and practically shouted to the world: "That's it, that's it! If these little microbes can enter the wine from the air—then they can also get into the body in the same way, *and cause an infection!*"

It was useless for him to discuss his theory with other doctors. While they respected his ability as a surgeon, they had no interest in his crazy ideas.

So Lister patiently set about searching for something that would be effective in fighting these germs—an *antiseptic* agent. And he soon found that carbolic acid was such a substance.

He was now ready to test his revolutionary theory. The perfect opportunity presented itself when young James Greenless was run over by a cart and brought to the hospital with a compound fracture of the leg. If this eleven-year-old boy had been treated by any other doctor in the world, he would have faced the certain loss of his leg. Maybe even death.

As the boy lay on the operating table, his face twisted by the pain, Lister tried to soothe him. "Now, Jimmy, we're going to put you to sleep, and you won't feel a thing. I know you want to be able to run and jump and play again, and I'm going to do everything I can to make that possible." Jimmy sensed that this

gentle, kind man really wanted to help him. And he drifted off happily into his anesthetic sleep.

Lister carefully cleansed the wound with carbolic acid. The instruments he used to set the broken bone and sew up the torn flesh had all been sterilized in the acid. The bandages were steeped in it. He had even used a crude device of his own invention to spray the air of the room with carbolic acid. Everything that could possibly come in contact with the patient had been completely sterilized.

Days went by. Jimmy's leg was healing—with no complications! One day, Dr. Lister came into Jimmy's room and said, "Well, son, how would you like to go home?"

Jimmy was ecstatic. He jumped out of bed and danced around the room. And Lister gazed at those

Jimmy . . . jumped out of bed and danced around the room.

two normal, energetic legs. All the riches of the world could have given him no more pleasure than this sight. And to think of the countless legs, and arms, and lives his discovery would save!

But it was no time to rest. One isolated case was hardly enough proof to support such a startling new theory. Lister began to use his antiseptic method on every patient; and then, after many operations, he developed irrefutable proof.

Recognition did not come easily. But gradually, doctors in other parts of Europe heard about his work and began to introduce antisepsis into *their* hospitals; although in Lister's homeland, England, there was little or no interest.

Lister continued his research work, always attempting to improve on his methods. Later on, he made triumphant tours of Europe and America, where he was enthusiastically hailed for his great contribution to medical science. Finally, England, too, recognized the value of his discovery, and heaped honors upon him.

Lister lived to see others go forward with his work. It was soon learned that the simplest way to kill bacteria was by the application of heat. So boiling water replaced the use of carbolic acid as a sterilizing agent.

And so it is that Joseph Lister, dedicated to the well-being of his fellow men, is justly called *The Father of Modern Surgery.*

ALEXANDER GRAHAM BELL

(1847-1922)

Inventor of the Telephone

ONE OF THE world's greatest inventors, Thomas Alva Edison, once said: "Genius is made up of 2 per cent inspiration and 98 per cent perspiration." By this he meant that even a genius can accomplish little without a good deal of plain hard work. There is no better illustration of this than the way in which Alexander Graham Bell arrived at the invention of the telephone.

Originally, Bell was a teacher of the deaf. With his great sympathy for the lonely plight of those who could not hear, he thought constantly about how he could help them to overcome their handicap. Upon learning of the existence of sound waves, it occurred to Bell that there might be a way to transform these waves into something that could be *seen*. He thought that if he could change the sounds heard over a telegraph wire into written marks of different lengths, a deaf person might be able to "hear" by seeing the marks. In other words, Bell hoped to transform sound waves into a kind of writing.

With this idea in mind, Bell began an intensive study of the science and mechanics of sound. He certainly had no idea that he was going to end up by inventing a telephone! For three long years, Bell and his assistant, Thomas A. Watson, experimented with sound waves. Time and again their painstaking work and experiments came to naught. Time and again they were forced to change their ideas, devise new theories and new techniques. And always, the work had to be done with extreme care.

At first, Bell was aided financially by the father of one of his pupils, a beautiful young deaf girl named Mabel Hubbard. She was later to become Bell's wife. As a loving father, Mr. Hubbard was eager to see the invention of a device which would help his daughter. As a man of imagination and courage, he was willing to take a chance on the ideas of Alexander Bell.

Realizing that the young teacher could not possibly earn enough money to buy the equipment he needed for his experiments, Mr. Hubbard offered to finance the experiments himself. But as failure followed failure, even the staunch Mr. Hubbard became discouraged and withdrew from the venture. Only Bell and the loyal Watson were left to continue the work.

Then quite unexpectedly, on a hot afternoon in June, 1875, the turning point came. Bell and Watson had set up their apparatus, each in a separate room. Watson was getting ready to send a telegraphic dot-dash message from one room to the other, when a little disc in his apparatus got stuck. He plucked the disc free.

Suddenly Bell, in his room, noticed an extraordinary thing! His receiving disc was vibrating and, as it vibrated, a faint musical note was sounding in his receiver! In high excitement, he shouted to Watson to pluck his disc once more. Watson did so, and again

. . . he spoke the first actual telephone message.

Bell saw the disc in his own room vibrate, and again he heard the faint musical sound! Then Bell knew for sure that the vibrations of the disc in Watson's room were causing the disc in his own room to vibrate. He realized that it was the wire connecting the two discs that transmitted the vibrations.

When the same vibrations were repeated by the disc in his own room, they produced the same sound. Instantly, Bell grasped the important principle he had accidentally discovered.

He had learned how to transmit sound from one place to another. If he could transmit one sound, he could transmit *any* sound—even the sound of words spoken by the human voice. From now on it would just be a matter of finding the right materials to make a sending apparatus (transmitter) and a receiving apparatus (receiver)—an instrument so sensitive that every fine variation of sound could be clearly heard.

He set to work immediately to construct an apparatus. Six months later, in the attic of his house, he spoke the first actual telephone message. And the words were clearly and unmistakably heard by Watson through the receiver, down in the cellar.

Now Bell took out a patent for his great invention. He was only in his twenties—but to this young man came fame, honor and wealth. His remarkable invention, the telephone, has brought the whole world closer together.

THOMAS ALVA EDISON

(1847-1931)

Wizard of Electricity

OF ALL the great inventors who ever lived, it is hard to compare any one to Thomas Alva Edison. Every time we switch on a light, make a phone call, go to the movies, listen to the radio or the phonograph, watch television, send a telegram, use a typewriter—the list could go on and on—we owe a "thank you" to this amazing man.

Thomas Edison worked hard—day and night—enthusiastically, excitedly and unceasingly. You have read elsewhere in this book that he once said: "Genius is 2 per cent inspiration and 98 per cent perspiration." He believed this to the roots of him and he acted accordingly all the 84 years of his life.

He was born in Milan, Ohio, in 1847 and died in

1931. Strange as it seems, he did very poorly at school. When he was seven, his teacher told his mother that the boy was so backward she simply could not teach him! Mrs. Edison thereupon took young Tom out of school, and she became his teacher.

When Tom was only twelve, he got himself a job selling newspapers and candy on the Grand Trunk Railway between Port Huron, Michigan, the town he lived in, and Detroit. Soon he added fruits and vegetables to his wares. His generous disposition won many friends for him among the railway workers. He was always deeply fascinated by science and he constantly read scientific books. Most of the money he earned he spent on books. He equipped a fine chemistry laboratory for himself. So that he wouldn't be wasting his time between stations, he also set up a chemistry laboratory on the train.

One day, as the train was bumping over a rough stretch of track, a jar of combustible material fell over and broke. It started a small fire among his newspapers. For this, Edison lost his job.

A few years before this episode, young Edison had saved the life of a little child by snatching him out of the path of an onrushing train. The child's father was a telegrapher. When he heard that Tom was out of work, he offered to teach him telegraphy.

Most boys of fifteen might have studied a few hours a day, but not Thomas Edison. The lad studied and practiced *eighteen hours a day!* He became a crack telegrapher—in fact one of the best that ever lived.

Before he was eighteen years old, young Thomas Edison had the great misfortune to become deaf. One might think his deafness would have hampered him in telegraphy. But Edison had an enormous faculty for concentration. He handled the telegraph set by sensing the vibration of the clicking instrument. In this way, he "heard" messages.

Edison never considered his deafness an obstacle. In fact, in later years when he was world-famous and had to attend long, boring dinners in his honor, he used to wisecrack about the advantages of being hard of hearing.

Edison got a job as a telegrapher. The young man's proficiency was extraordinary. It was tested one day in an exciting manner.

He had decided to go to the big city of Boston and get a job as telegrapher there. When he applied for the position in his shabby clothes, he did not make a very good impression. But it was decided to give him a "chance." The other telegraphers hatched a little plot against him. As he sat down at the desk, a group of operators gathered round to watch the fun. The New York operator, who was in on the joke, started sending out messages at a normal pace. Then he began to increase his speed, abbreviating long words which Edison had to write out fully. Soon the messages were

The operators admiringly congratulated the young man.

coming in at a breakneck pace, faster than messages were ever normally sent. Without pausing, young Edison kept transcribing the messages into writing. The ordeal was kept up for four solid hours! Finally, the operators gave up and admiringly congratulated the young man for his efficiency and good humor.

After a short time at the Boston job, Tom decided to work on the night shift. He wanted to have time during the day for activity in a machine shop. There, he could carry out all kinds of experiments. He kept a careful record of the results of his experiments in notebooks. This habit of keeping notebooks was never interrupted. During his lifetime, Edison filled more than 2,500 of them!

He was only twenty-one years old when he applied for his first patent. His invention was an electrical vote recorder. This instrument could keep a record of each legislator's vote in Congress just by the pressing of a button instead of the lengthy process of calling the roll. That same year, he devised a method for sending two telegraphic messages over the same wire at the same time. He was so excited about this invention that he quit his job in Boston, and spent all his money setting up a demonstration. Something went wrong with the demonstration and Edison lost almost every penny he had in the world. He had just enough money left to go to New York City.

Since he had no money for lodging, a friend found

him a most unusual place to sleep at no cost at all. This was the boiler room of the Gold Exchange. There was a cot down in the basement, next to the master transmitter. After hunting for a job during the day, Edison spent the first two evenings studying the complicated mechanism of the transmitter. On the third morning, just as he was going out, great excitement broke out on the floor of the Exchange. It seems that the master transmitter had broken down. This transmitter sent out the records of the changing prices on the Gold Exchange. Without it, the brokers could not make contact with their customers.

When Edison heard what all the noise was about, he brought the manager down to the basement and calmly pointed out what was wrong.

"The contact spring is broken," he said. "It must have fallen down through the gears."

"Who are you?" exclaimed the manager. "Anyway, can you fix it?"

Edison rolled up his sleeves and set to work. Within two hours he had the transmitter working perfectly.

He was hired on the spot; and from then on, he had a job as Technical Superintendent of the Gold Exchange at the then fabulous salary of $300 a month!

Pretty soon Edison cast his eye on the ticker-tape machines. He simply couldn't resist figuring out how to improve them, and he showed his ideas for improvement to General Lefferts of the Gold and Stock

Telegraph Company. General Lefferts was so impressed with the twenty-one-year-old inventor that he offered him a job in a company that made stock-ticker instruments. It wasn't long before Edison had designed another instrument, which he called the Edison Universal Printer. When he saw it, General Lefferts' eyes popped with excitement.

"How much do you want for your printer?" he asked.

Edison was wondering whether he should ask for $3,000 or $4,000. He did not dare take a chance, and said instead, "I don't know, General. What do you offer?"

"How about $40,000?" said the General. Edison, stunned and thrilled, gasped his agreement.

Now, at the age of twenty-two, Thomas Edison became a successful manufacturer of his own inventions. His success never went to his head. In fact, anyone visiting his plant would have found it hard to pick out who was the boss and who were the workers. For Edison was always right in the middle of things, with his sleeves rolled up, working along with his employees.

For most people, running a large factory would be a full-time job. But not to Tom Edison. His head was full of dozens of ideas. Soon he was working on not less than forty inventions at one time! He not only created completely new ideas, but he improved and perfected other people's ideas.

Edison . . . pulled the switch and the windows . . .
suddenly blazed into light.

For instance, Alexander Graham Bell had invented the first telephone. But Bell's telephone was impractical for many purposes. It was Edison who developed and patented the special transmitter which was so effective and inexpensive that the telephone became what it is today.

His improvements of the typewriter were just as important.

Edison's greatest creation was, without doubt, the electric-light bulb. Edison worked for five long years on this invention. He tested more than 6,000 varieties of plant and vegetable fibres before he finally found the material from which to make the thin, thread-like filament inside the bulb. He poured all the money he had earned into countless experiments to perfect the incandescent lamp.

When the historic moment arrived and he finally succeeded, he realized that inventing the bulb was only the first step. He now had to build a whole system to bring power from large electric generators through wires into people's homes. This was a stupendous task. But Edison staked all he had on a test. He announced he would set up a complete electric lighting system in one square mile of New York City.

On Monday, September 4, 1882, the remarkable experiment was ready. Edison stood at the master switch. At the given instant, he pulled the switch and the windows of a whole downtown district suddenly blazed into light. The new *Age of Light* had begun!

Great as was his invention of the electric-light bulb, who can measure the joy that he brought to the world with his other wonder—the phonograph. Possibly even more than the electric-light bulb, the invention of the talking machine made Edison's name world-famous.

It would take pages just to list all of the inventions of Thomas Edison. By his labor and his genius, he has lessened people's work and brought joy into homes the world over. All mankind owes Thomas Alva Edison a tribute of everlasting gratitude and honor.

WALTER REED

(1851-1902)

Enemy of Yellow Fever

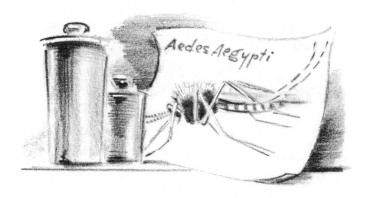

YELLOW JACK — A thrill of horror gripped anyone who heard the words! That was the name given to the dread disease of yellow fever. Year after year, thousands of people died of it.

In 1900, the American Army was in Cuba fighting with the Cubans against the Spanish. But *Yellow Jack* killed many more soldiers than did the guns of war. Thousands died and thousands more lay dying.

What caused this terrible sickness? No one knew. Some people said it came from the mist that rose from the swamps. Some said that it came from tropical heat. Some people thought that the way to stop it was to burn all the clothes that were worn by people who had had the disease. Others said that all the houses in which the yellow fever victims had lived ought to be burned down. But there could be no agreement, because no one really *knew* how it started, or what to do about it.

No one except a man in Havana—Dr. Carlos Finlay. He said, "You are all wrong—yellow fever is caused by a certain mosquito." But no one believed him. All the doctors and research scientists were trying to find the *germ* of yellow fever.

Because so many American soldiers in Cuba were dying of the disease, the United States Army sent a doctor, Walter Reed, down to Cuba to see what he could do. Major Reed visited the sick soldiers and he also visited patients in the Cuban hospitals. Then he went into people's homes and examined the food they ate, the water they drank, how their houses were built. He couldn't understand why some persons got yellow fever, and others, living in the same house with them, did not.

Then he went to see Dr. Finlay and listened to his explanation. Dr. Finlay said, "This mosquito bites a person who has yellow fever. What does a mosquito do when it bites? It drinks the blood of the person it bites. Then it flies over to another person who doesn't have yellow fever, and bites him. In this way, it injects the germs of the sick person into the body of the well person. Nobody catches yellow fever by touching someone who has it, or by wearing the sick person's clothes, or anything like that. Don't waste

"Kill off these mosquitoes and you will kill off yellow fever."

your time trying to find out what the germ is. Kill off these mosquitoes and you will kill off yellow fever."

This sounded sensible to Walter Reed, but how could he prove it? Then up spoke his assistants, Jesse Lazear and James Carroll. "Try us!" they said. "Let mosquitoes who have bitten sick people bite us."

"Do you know what you are saying?" asked Major Reed. "You may die. We possess no cure for yellow fever, and more than half of the people who get the disease die."

"We will never find a cure unless we try," they answered.

Jesse Lazear was the first one. He went to a hospital where men were dying of yellow fever. He took some mosquitoes with him and had them bite some of the sick men. Then he placed the insects on his own arm and let them bite him.

James Carroll did the same. But the trouble was that although James Carroll got yellow fever, Jesse Lazear did not. Not this time. So they couldn't prove that the mosquito was the carrier of the disease. After all, they thought, maybe Carroll got the disease in some other way. Maybe he had caught it from having touched the bedclothes on which a yellow fever victim had lain.

James Carroll almost died, but he finally recovered. And nothing had been proved. Everybody still believed that the clothing and bedding of yellow fever victims were deadly. So Walter Reed set out to find if it was true.

He had two little houses built far away from any town. He had very good screens fastened on all the doors and windows so that no mosquitoes could possibly get in. Then he shut the doors and windows tight. Into one house he brought the dirty bedclothes and pajamas of men who had died or were dying of yellow fever. He kept the little house overheated and made damp with steaming tubs of water.

Into this smelly, suffocating house stepped three of the most heroic men in all history—Warren Jernegan, Levi Folk, and Doctor Cooke. For twenty days and nights they remained there, sleeping on filthy beds, wearing clothes taken from men who had died or were sick with yellow fever.

After almost three weeks, they came out. Not one of them had caught yellow fever! In order to be absolutely sure, Walter Reed sent in six more men to do the same thing. The names of these courageous soldiers of science are hardly known. They were willing to risk death in order to save other people's lives. But none of the men who spent those horrible nights in that awful house became ill.

Now Walter Reed was ready for the next part of the test. The other little house was nice and clean. It had two rooms. Both were cool and airy and well-screened, for Major Reed didn't want any *stray* mos-

Into this smelly, suffocating house stepped three of the most heroic men in the world.

quitoes or other insects to get into this house. In this house he only wanted mosquitoes which he had fed on the blood of yellow fever victims.

Then a young man named John J. Moran walked into one room of that clean little house. He had just taken a bath. The bedclothes were spotless and his pajamas freshly washed. But waiting for him in the room were fifteen fever-infected mosquitoes which pounced on him the minute he entered.

The other room was exactly like his—clean and airy. Two other young men were in there. But no mosquitoes were allowed to get into their room.

John J. Moran and the other two men stayed in that house for the same length of time. Then, on Christmas morning, 1900, Moran came down with a terrible case of yellow fever.

Thus it was proved that the dirty little house, full of soiled clothes from people who had died of yellow fever—but with *no* mosquitoes—was safe; and the spotlessly clean house—*with* mosquitoes—was deadly.

Now, at last, people knew what to do to stop the disease—wipe out the yellow-fever-carrying mosquitoes which infested the swamps! This was done so well that today there are practically no cases of yellow fever!

But let us never forget Walter Reed and those heroic men who risked their lives to find out the cause of the fearful *Yellow Jack.*

LUTHER BURBANK

(1849-1926)

Wizard of Plant Growth

"IF" IS THAT powerful little word on which many important events of our world hinge. For example, *if* Luther Burbank had not read a certain book as a young man, he might never have chosen the career which has made our gardens more beautiful, our fruits and vegetables finer and larger. This is what he said of himself:

"When I was nineteen, in 1868, probably the turning point of my career in fixing my life work in the production of new species and varieties of plant life was the reading of Darwin's *Variation of Animals and Plants Under Domestication.*"

Now that's a sober-sounding title, and most people wouldn't be likely to pick it from the library shelf. But young Burbank was already interested in nature, and into his fertile mind this book planted a seed so inspiring that he spent the rest of his life cultivating it.

Luther was born in 1849, in Lancaster, Massachusetts, the thirteenth child of the family. His father was a farmer, but also a brick and pottery maker on a small scale.

From his mother, he inherited a love of nature. She adored flowers and birds, and all growing things. From his father, he learned to work with his hands. In his teens he was a wood turner and pattern maker. His quick mind often evolved a better or faster way of performing his tasks. But his hidden talents as a horticulturist and botanist were awakened by Darwin's book.

At nineteen, he bought a 17-acre farm in Lunenburg, Massachusetts. He wanted to experiment at crossbreeding plants, and he soon made a successful business of the farm. His genius at raising fruits, flowers, and vegetables became quickly known. Luther's produce was not only first to reach the market, but it was of superior quality. The vegetables and fruits were larger, juicier or crisper, and of much better color and flavor than those of other growers. On this farm, he created the famous Burbank potato, the first experimental product of a lifework that would make him famous as a plant wizard for generations to come.

Though he had no college education, nor any formal scientific training, Burbank had tremendous native intelligence. He was a student who learned by doing, rather than by bookish theories. Possessed of imagination and infinite patience, he could think of, and then attempt, endless experiments. And although he was not an artist, he had great artistic feeling which showed in the products he developed.

On his first farm Luther observed a peculiar potato plant. He saw a seed ball, a rare thing, on the side of the plant, *above* ground. He carefully picked it up, and in a special plot raised the seeds from this vine. Some seeds grew up into poor and spindly plants. Some were ordinary. But by selection and special attention, he developed the fine Burbank potato.

Now he wanted to go to California, for that state, with its long growing season, would be best for his experiments. He sold the rights to his potato, and he also sold his farm. His profits were very small, but with these slender funds he traveled to Santa Rosa, California.

The long trip took nine days and nights. He slept in a day coach, and lived on the contents of a large basket packed by his tearful mother and sister. His letters home, however, soon showed his anxious family how delighted he was with his new surroundings.

In one he wrote: "I firmly believe from what I have seen that California is the chosen spot of all the earth as far as nature is concerned . . . the climate is perfect . . . the air is so sweet that it is a pleasure to drink it in.

The sunshine is pure and soft, the mountains which gird the valley are lovely."

Settled now in this gardener's heaven, Burbank went on to make his creations known throughout the world. He obtained his astounding results by selecting and crossing his choice of two plants to produce a third type. This he did by placing the pollen of one flower on the pistil of another, and then letting Nature take over.

Roses, lilies, dahlias, poppies, petunias, and many other flowers responded to his efforts. His most famous flower, however, was the Shasta daisy. Crossing the English daisy, the wild American variety, and a pure white Japanese cousin, he created the lovely flower we know today. He named it for his favorite snowcapped peak in the Sierra Mountains. If your mother has a garden, she probably has many flower varieties created or improved by Burbank. The next time you walk through a garden, take special notice of them.

Burbank always had several thousand plants under constant observation. Some projects took years to complete to his satisfaction. But he knew that when man works in partnership with Nature, he cannot hurry her —too much.

His work with plums, berries, and lilies was outstanding. The *plumcot*, a cross of plum and apricot, is a delicious fruit. The giant Amaryllis is his creation, as well as the *pomato*.

Burbank's greatest contribution to the science of growing things was his demonstration of the value of patience in crossbreeding. But, although he performed thousands of experiments, he did not take the time to write down his findings in each case. This has been a great loss to other horticulturists, who would have found his data of immense interest and value.

. . . Burbank grew hundreds of varieties of cherries on a single tree!

Although he did not enjoy good health, Burbank was so diligent that he produced fabulous results. He developed the white blackberry, the loganberry, new kinds of chestnuts and walnuts. Luther Burbank also evolved a plum without a pit, and one that tasted like a Bartlett pear!

On one occasion, just as a demonstration, Burbank grew hundreds of varieties of cherries on a single tree! His uncanny sense of crossbreeding, and his patience at trial and error experiments made him the greatest American horticulturist and botanist.

Burbank was not interested in theories. He used the "try it" method. During his lifetime he developed 220 varieties of fruits, flowers, trees, vegetables, and grasses.

A serious, earnest worker, he was not without a sense of humor. One day, as he was walking through his garden, a friend asked him, "What are you working on now, Luther?"

"I'm trying to cross an eggplant with a milkweed," Burbank replied.

"What on earth do you expect to get out of that?" asked his astonished visitor.

"Custard pie," replied Burbank with a twinkle in his eye.

Luther Burbank richly deserves his fame as a botanist. He earned it through a lifetime of love for growing things, by his patience, his careful observations—and plain hard work.

THE CURIES

(PIERRE: 1859-1906; MARIE: 1867-1934)

The Story of Radium

PIERRE CURIE looked ruefully at the two shiny new bicycles.

"How could you do it, Marie?" he asked tenderly. "You should not have used your money for them. The money was given to you for your trousseau, and you have spent it on bicycles!"

"Pooh," Marie answered airily. "What do dresses matter! Just think, Pierre, if it weren't for the bicycles we would have to spend our honeymoon in our room. But with them, we can travel all over France whenever we can take the time for a trip."

To tell the truth, pretty dresses meant very little to Marie Sklodowska. At her home in Poland, there hadn't been much money for finery. And anyway, she cared a great deal more about her studies than she did about clothes. She loved her studies so much that she finished high school when she was only fifteen! Even though she was so young, she obtained employment as a governess. She made a very pretty one, too.

A few years later, after saving as much money as she could, she went to Paris to specialize in mathematics and chemistry. There she met Pierre. Within a year they were married. Then, it seemed, hard times really began.

Although Pierre was a brilliant scholar, he lacked certain academic degrees. And so he was prevented from teaching in schools where he would have earned a large salary. They were very poor, and, when their first child was born, the struggle to make ends meet became even more trying.

Besides their baby and each other, Marie and Pierre cared about just one thing: they wanted to do chemical research. For this, they needed a laboratory. Sometimes they went hungry in order to buy a piece of equipment they needed for their experiments.

The problem of where to find a building they could use as a laboratory was difficult. Finally, they took a dilapidated old shack; it was the only place they could afford.

One night the rain poured down in torrents. It beat steadily against the windows and roof. Inside the shack, Marie and Pierre worked feverishly over a long wooden table on which there were tubes, flasks, and a small burner. Their faces were intent as Pierre held a dish of dark, sticky substance up to the light. Suddenly, a stream of water poured down through a hole in the roof and spattered into the dish. Pierre threw the dish onto the table in disgust, sat down on a crude wooden chair, and put his head in his hands.

"How can we work here, Marie? What kind of laboratory is this, where the rain comes through the rotting roof? How are we to do *anything?*" His voice was filled with despair.

Marie was cold and tired. But she went over to Pierre and put her arm around his shoulder. "Never mind, *chéri.* Don't let the rain bother you." Her voice was soothing and gentle. She spoke as she might to a weeping child. "Why, look, our little Irene doesn't mind the rain."

Pierre looked up to see a thin stream of water dripping on his tiny daughter as she slept in her crib next to the table. He smiled in spite of himself. The drops rolled off the baby's limp hand. She didn't even move.

"You're right, Marie. If the rain doesn't disturb our *bébé,* why should I let it bother me?" Pierre got to his feet and moved the crib away from the leak.

Together, they returned to their laboratory table to take up the work where they had left off. Marie prepared another dish of the same chemical.

To Marie Curie, the poor, meager life she led with

her husband and baby was nothing to complain about. As a child in Poland, she had often experienced cold and hunger. Now, at least, she was in France. She had educated herself. She had Pierre, to whom she was completely devoted. And together they were sharing their work and their dreams.

"Some day," Marie murmured, "this will all be an amusing memory. We will tell our friends about this leaking roof and they will laugh with us. Then you will have a shining laboratory with every new device. You will be famous and respected."

"We shall see," said Pierre, adding a new chemical to the dish.

Silently, Marie and Pierre watched, their faces tense. Marie transferred the substance into a beaker of acid. A cloud of vapor rose from the vessel. Then she poured the liquid through a filter. What remained, Pierre placed on a clean dish. The young chemists stared at it, excitedly.

The tiny bit of matter glowed!

Straightening up, they looked at each other without a word. Then, suddenly, Pierre threw his arms into the air. "We were right! We have it! We have it at last!" he shouted.

His joy knew no bounds. He took Marie by the waist and danced her about the room. They laughed, then cried with delight.

A sound from Irene stopped them. Picking up the

The tiny bit of matter glowed!

child, Marie smiled at it. "This is the greatest of all nights, my darling," she said to the baby. "Some day you will understand what has happened here tonight." Holding the child, Marie waltzed over the damp, muddy floor.

Neither Marie nor Pierre heard the loud knocking on the door of the shack, so joyous was their celebration. They did not even notice the man who came in, until he spoke.

"What is the meaning of all this noise?" the man asked. "Are you going crazy?"

"Crazy with happiness, m'sieur," Pierre answered, going to his neighbor and shaking him warmly by the hand.

"Ah, you have won the lottery?" the neighbor said.

"Far better than that, m'sieur," Marie said, taking the man by the arm and leading him over to the worktable. "Do you know what is in that dish, m'sieur?"

The man bent over to look more closely. "Is it my imagination, Madame Curie, or is that chemical glowing?"

"It is really glowing, m'sieur. You do not imagine it. It is the first radioactive element that has ever been isolated," Pierre said.

"But what is it called?" the man asked.

"We will call it *radium,* m'sieur," Marie said.

The man rubbed his chin doubtfully. "Is this an important discovery, madame?"

Marie nodded her head. "Then I congratulate you," the neighbor said. "You will be rich. But you must be careful to protect this discovery. There are many who would steal it from you."

"No," answered Marie solemnly. "If we succeeded, Pierre and I always planned to give radium to the world. It is for the good of all the people of the earth that we have worked. We could not be selfish with so powerful a force."

Marie and Pierre Curie kept their promise. They released the secret of their discovery to the world. Immediately, honor and fame were theirs. Pierre was appointed to the science faculty of the Sorbonne, the greatest of French universities.

Some years later, Pierre died in a traffic accident, and Marie was chosen to fill his position at the university. She became the first woman ever to hold such a post; and although Pierre was no longer with her, she continued his work.

The laboratory they had dreamed of became a reality. It was a fitting memorial to the man she loved so dearly. Here, research on radium was, and still is, carried on. One important use of radium is to check cancer.

During World War I, Marie outfitted twenty radiological cars, and with them she personally visited hospitals and ambulance stations in the battle zones. Some time later, Marie was awarded the Nobel prize for

. . . Marie . . . visited hospitals and ambulance
stations in the battle zones.

chemistry, the highest honor that can come to a chemist.

In 1921, in appreciation of her work and so that she might do further research, the women of America gave her a gift of radium. It was only a single gram—about one twenty-eighth of an ounce—but it was worth $120,000!

Because the Curies were willing to work under the most discouraging conditions, countless lives have been saved. And because of their industry and spirit, we now stand on the threshold of a new age, the *Atomic Era,* a time when undreamed-of benefits may come to man.

GEORGE W. CARVER

(c. 1864-1943)

Trailblazer in Agriculture

THIS IS THE story of a man who was born a slave, yet who grew up to be one of the greatest naturalists and scientists in the world. This is the story of a boy who disregarded the handicap of his lowly birth, and who by sheer will developed himself into a great man.

No one knows the exact date when George Washington Carver was born, because he was not considered important enough to have his birth date recorded. The year of his birth has been estimated to be about 1864, since it *is* known that he was born during the Civil War period. His father and mother were Negro slaves in Diamond Grove, Missouri, where little George first saw the light of day.

In those disturbed times, there were bitter argu-

ments for and against slavery, and many terrifying
things happened. One of the worst things that could
ever happen to a young baby happened to George—
his mother was kidnaped by slave traders. She was
never heard of again.

While George was still a little tot, his father died.
The Carver family, who had owned his mother,
adopted the little orphan. They were good, kind people, and they brought George up very lovingly. They
taught him the ways of a farm and the household
chores that were part of everyday living. If the little
boy had to work hard, he worked no harder than
they themselves did.

Mr. Carver taught the youngster how to plant corn,
how to hunt, how to fish, how to gather wild honey,
how to care for horses, and how to tend other farm
animals. Mrs. Carver taught young George how to
cultivate a vegetable garden, how to cook, how to
sew, and how to bake. She even taught him how to
wash and iron clothes.

Even when George was a little boy, he loved all
growing things. Everything he touched seemed to
bloom. He was always asking questions about plants
and flowers—questions which neither Mr. nor Mrs.
Carver was able to answer. If only he could read, he
thought. If only he could unlock the secrets that lay
in books. How much he wanted to go to school!

But the school in this village of Diamond Grove,

Missouri, did not accept Negro students, and George's yearning to master the printed word remained unfulfilled. Then one day, while the Carvers were doing their spring cleaning, they found a little spelling book. George was full of excitement. Mrs. Carver started him off learning how to read, and George studied the little speller constantly. Within a few months, he had mastered it completely. But that was the end of the road—at least for the time being. There was no other book at hand.

A few years later, the Carvers heard of a school for Negro children that had been opened in another town. Even though they needed George on the farm, they had no thought of denying him the education he craved. They had no money to give; all they could bestow upon him was their blessing and their heartfelt and sage advice.

"Don't be afraid to ask for work," said Mr. Carver to the ten-year-old boy. "You are good in every kind of work on the farm." "Yes," joined in Mrs. Carver, "and you can cook and sew and launder as well as the best housewife."

And so the little Negro boy set out without money, without anything except the clothes on his back and a little food to eat on the way—set out to go to school. Even if he were admitted, he would have to support himself. He would have to provide himself with food, clothing, shelter—in short, everything that a child usually gets from his parents without even thinking about it. After school, George always had a full hard day's work before him. He did most of his studying at night when he was tired. Yet, in spite of this enormous handicap, he was practically always the best student in his class.

When George had completed his meager schooling in the little Missouri town, he wanted to go to college. What an idle dream! No college within any reasonable distance would accept a Negro.

But after many long years, when George was a grown man, he finally gained admission to Simpson College in Iowa, the first Negro ever to be so distinguished. Here, too, he became an honor student. Because of his fine record, upon graduation he was recommended to the Iowa State Agricultural College.

And now for the first time, George Washington Carver learned about the things that had always been closest to his heart. Here, he began to get some answers to the questions that had stirred him as a boy. Carver was no longer a youngster, yet he reacted with the excitement of a child. He learned about plants and he learned about animals, and he learned about many other things. He learned how minerals enriched the earth, how the earth nourished plants, and how plants provided food for animals.

He was eager to put his newfound knowledge to work in a practical way. He saw how the poverty-stricken farmers of the South lost their crops because of insect plagues; he saw the backbreaking toil that led to little reward because of poor soil conditions; he saw how drought and the lack of irrigation dried up and brought ruin to the land—regardless of many years' effort.

How could he—George Washington Carver—save these poor people from poverty and disaster? How could he help them overcome their age-old problems? These were the thoughts that constantly occupied his mind, this was the goal to which he now dedicated his life.

After he was graduated from Iowa State Agricul-

He taught them how to plant crops . . .

tural College, Carver was offered a professorship at that institution. The director of the school invited him to become his assistant in experimental work and in original research. No gift in the power of man could have made Carver any happier. Now, at long last, he could carry out the tests, ideas, and theories which he had thought about for years.

At the Experimental Station of Iowa State, there were large fields planted with all kinds of botanical specimens. Here, one could watch insects just as if they were in a laboratory; one could see how the pests behaved; one could test out insecticides.

At the Experimental Station there were also rolling, grassy meadows, and many cattle. Here, one could carry on experiments in breeding. One could test conditions which would produce ticks and animal lice, and one could try out cures for the terrible diseases that killed large herds of cattle.

Here, with the help of other professors and agricultural experts, Carver and his co-workers developed new methods for improving crops and new ways to keep farm animals in good health.

Now, after many years of hardship, Carver had achieved what for him was an ideally happy life. Each and every day was filled with learning. Here he was free to develop fresh ideas. He received a handsome salary; he lived in comfort; his name was honored and respected.

And then, into the tranquility of this wonderful life came a call which he could not deny. Tuskegee Institute in Alabama, the only institution in the South providing higher education for Negroes, beckoned to him. This institution had been founded by the great Negro educator, Booker T. Washington.

The administrators there, when they heard of the fame of George Washington Carver, invited him to come to Tuskegee and teach other Negroes. Tuskegee was a poor, small school. It had no famous professors. It had practically no equipment. There was no money at Tuskegee. There were no scientists with whom he could share his ideas. In fact, his salary would be cut miserably. The entire institute consisted of two small buildings, and the students who studied there had little educational background.

Carver responded instantly to the call of his people. He forgot about his own comfort. All that he wanted was that the young people of his race be given a chance to make their lives meaningful.

This was his dream. But when Carver came to Tuskegee in 1897, his heart sank. The school was situated on an old plantation that had gone to rack and ruin. The topsoil was washed away. There was really nothing to work with—almost nothing to start with.

But Tuskegee had picked the right man. All his life Carver had worked hard, had been forced to make do with little. He showed himself to be an inspiring leader. He organized his students into little groups. He had them scour the countryside for odd bits of metal. With this scrap, they made farm implements. He had them go to the swamps and load carts with swamp muck. He had them spread this rich soil over the desolate land. He taught them how to plant and rotate crops, and showed them labor was a thing to enjoy. Soon, Tuskegee had blooming fields, and the face of the institute was changed.

Then, George Washington Carver set out to change the face of the *entire* Southland. The once rich cotton plantations were now barren and unfruitful. Part was due to destruction caused by the Civil War, part due to the loss in manpower and consequent improper care. But Carver believed that the main cause of the terrible decline in crop production was that the fields had become worn out. The mineral content of the soil, he claimed, was gone.

Carver found it extremely difficult to make people heed his warnings. Cotton could be sold for cash. People needed cash money to buy things. An acre of land that had once produced a bale of cotton now produced only a quarter as much. Yet the farmers who planted cotton wanted the little money that the cotton crop would yield. They stubbornly kept following the ways of their fathers. They refused to plant anything but cotton. Slowly and patiently, Carver began to persuade people that there were other crops which would bring money. He taught them how to plant peanuts, how to raise sweet potatoes. And it was these two crops that saved the South from disaster.

George Washington Carver developed 301 products from the peanut plant. Then he showed that the sweet potato could yield 118 useful substances. From the peanut plant, he made twine, dyes, hog food, peanut oil, and scores of other things. From sweet potatoes, he made fiber, flour, and dozens of other materials. He wrote hundreds of small pamphlets describing the advantages of growing these two particular plants. In short, he showed farmers that they could make a living if they grew cotton one year, peanuts the next; that the rotation of crops would keep the soil in robust condition.

But many poor people in the South, both white and black, were not able to read. What good were these pamphlets to people who could not be reached by the printed word? So Carver set up a *School on Wheels.* He outfitted a wagon with all kinds of botanical exhibits, farm equipment, and simple setups for experiments. With a few associates, he traveled from village to village, and wherever he stopped, he held a meeting, using samples and models to demonstrate his ideas. He was friendly, and spoke in the simple, homespun language of the country folk.

Soon the fame of his *School on Wheels* spread. Other, larger schools and universities copied his experi-

ment. The idea, in time, reached the Government.
Today, the U. S. Department of Agriculture has a special division which issues booklets of guidance on every
subject that has to do with farming. The Department
of Agriculture also maintains a small army of experts
to instruct farmers and to discuss their problems with
them.

Carver set up a School on Wheels.

Carver also found out how nourishing and useful the soy bean was in China. So he brought this plant to America, where it has become a major crop.

He was the adventurous forerunner of the theory of extracting plastic materials from plants. The discoveries that Carver developed are too numerous to mention. But it is sufficient tribute to the power of his genius to record that illustrious world leaders and giants of industry came to do honor to this humble man in his home at Tuskegee. Theodore Roosevelt, when he was President of the United States; Franklin Delano Roosevelt, when he was President of the United States; Henry Ford; Thomas Alva Edison; the Crown Prince of Sweden—these were some of the renowned of the earth who saluted this Negro as one of the world's greatest scientists.

For now the ideas of this man—born a slave—were heard in the four corners of the earth. From Europe to Asia, from Africa to Australia, his advice was sought. Now Tuskegee became world-famous; and with the spread of its fame, there flowed into this house of learning financial support to carry on and to extend its work.

Ten years after his death in 1943, the United States Government acquired the farm in Missouri on which George Washington Carver was born. In 1953, this farm was dedicated as a permanent shrine to his memory.

THE WRIGHT BROTHERS

(WILBUR: 1867-1912; ORVILLE: 1871-1948)

Pioneers of Flight

THE COLD WIND swept across the desolate beach near Kitty Hawk, North Carolina. At first glance, one saw only a desolate, bleak strip of beach, dotted with sand dunes. But in one spot there stood five people staring curiously at a strange machine. The forty-foot wings made it look like some giant bird. Unlike a bird, though, it had an engine and two propellers. And lying flat on the lower wing, there was *a man!*

The few spectators were uncertain of just what they could expect to see. One of them, a jolly man named Tom Stuart, was roaring with laughter. "Do those fool boys really believe they're gonna take off and fly in that crazy-looking machine?" he said to his companions. "Well, now, I've heard some wild things in my time, but this just about takes the prize. I suspect they might be just a bit touched in the head."

Bill Tate, the village postmaster, spoke up. "Hold on there, Tom. Don't you go laughing at something just 'cause it's new to you. I don't know much about machines and flying and all that; but I do know these Wright brothers are mighty fine boys, and I got a lot of confidence in them."

"Who are they, anyway, and where did they come from?" someone else asked. "I don't recollect ever seeing them in town."

"Well, this is the third year they've been back here working on their flying machine," answered Bill Tate. "Their names are Wilbur and Orville Wright, and they come from Dayton, Ohio, where they run a bicycle shop. I don't know what ever got them off their bicycles and up into the air, but they won't stop till they get that machine to fly. Last year, and the year before last, they spent the summers here on this beach testing out gliders they built. 'Course, they just started off at the top of a dune and then glided down to the ground below. But this time they've got themselves an engine on that contraption, and they say it's gonna lift the machine right off the ground."

"Well, they'll just have to show me before I'll believe it," Tom said, still laughing. "And then maybe I'll go buy myself a pair of spectacles, 'cause I'll know I've been seeing things. No man's ever flown like a bird before, and none ever will. God gave birds wings and men feet—and that's why we're walking."

Just then they heard the roar of a motor, and then a shout. "Ready to take off, Orville?" Wilbur called to his brother, who was stretched out on the wing of the plane.

"Let her go!" replied Orville.

And as the small group of people watched in astonishment, they saw a miracle take place. After running the motor a few minutes to let it warm up, Orville released the wire holding the machine to the track. It started forward into the wind, and Wilbur ran alongside trying to help balance it. After a forty-foot run, the machine lifted into the air and actually flew!

Though it stayed aloft for only twelve seconds, this was the first time in the history of the world that a machine carrying a man had raised itself by its own power into the air in full flight, sailed forward without a reduction in speed, and finally landed at a point as high as that from which it had started.

This historic event took place on December 17, 1903. For the Wright brothers, it was the climax of years of hard work in trying to fulfill man's eternal dream of flying.

They had first become obsessed with this dream as little boys, when their father brought home a new toy. Holding it behind his back, he said, "Guess what I have here, boys!"

. . . the machine . . . actually flew!

But before they could guess, he released a little object that immediately shot up to the ceiling, and then fell to the floor. They were astounded. The toy was a primitive little *helicopter* made of paper, bamboo, and cork, with a rubber band that turned a small propeller.

The boys played with their helicopter for hours on end, watching it whizzing through the air. Then Wilbur had a wonderful idea. He said to his brother, "Orville, if this little thing can fly up to the ceiling, why don't we make a much bigger one that will fly way up into the clouds?"

They were both delighted with this prospect. So the little mechanics proceeded to build their first flying machine. But success could hardly have come this early. They soon discovered one of the basic principles of flying—a machine twice as big as another requires not twice but *eight* times as much power to lift it!

Though they became discouraged in their attempts to build a bigger helicopter, Wilbur and Orville did spend much of their boyhood making and flying kites. And often, as they watched the kites soaring through the air with the greatest of ease, they must have wondered whether someday they, too, might achieve flight.

The Wright brothers developed into highly skilled mechanics, so when the time came to earn a living, they opened a bicycle shop. But their interest in flying was increased as they heard of the various attempts

being made in Europe and America. And soon they were once again making plans to build their own flying machine. Only this time they went about it in a more scientific way. They read all the available accounts of previous experiments, carefully studied every aspect of the problem, and designed a glider in which to make their first try.

Kitty Hawk was chosen as the best location for test flights because the wind conditions there were favorable. During the first two summers, they made numerous glider flights, constantly checking and rechecking each factor. At times, there were hair-raising brushes with death when the machine crashed instead of landing properly. But they remained steadfast in their determination. By the third year, they had added an engine and propellers and were ready for their great moment.

After the first successful power flights at Kitty Hawk, the Wrights returned to Dayton and continued to work on and test their flying machine. In 1904, they made more than fifty flights, two of which lasted as long as five minutes each. Gradually, the world was beginning to realize that flying was not just a possibility—it was a fact. People no longer laughed and made jokes about that "crazy flying machine." The Wrights demonstrated their airplane in Paris and in Washington in 1908, and were greeted with enthusiastic acclaim in both capitals.

Once the Wright brothers had blazed the trail, a whole army of flyers, aircraft builders, and inventors sprang up to follow. In a matter of just a few years, a network of air traffic had been set up that linked practically every spot on the globe. Today, the modern jet airliner can carry us thousands of miles in just a few hours. The men responsible for this great achievement are remembered at the scene of their first historic flight, in Kitty Hawk, with this inscription:

IN COMMEMORATION OF THE
CONQUEST OF THE AIR
BY THE BROTHERS WILBUR AND ORVILLE WRIGHT.
CONCEIVED BY GENIUS, ACHIEVED BY DAUNTLESS
RESOLUTION AND UNCONQUERABLE FAITH.

FREDERICK BANTING

(1891-1941)

Discoverer of Insulin

ONLY FORTY years ago, *diabetes* was described as "one of the fatal diseases—remedy unknown." Today, millions of diabetics live long, normal, happy lives. The man who brought about this striking and wonderful change was a young Canadian surgeon, Frederick G. Banting, who, before becoming interested in diabetes, had never previously performed any independent research and had no special knowledge of the disease.

Fred Banting served as a captain in the Medical Corps during World War I. He never forgot the horrible suffering and slaughter he witnessed on the battlefields of Europe. As a surgeon, his job was to patch up broken limbs and shattered bodies. He did the best he could, but thousands of gallant young soldiers were beyond help. When the war ended, he knew that he wanted to spend the rest of his life helping mankind in the constant battle against death. He found that diabetes claimed more lives—and in just as cruel a way—than did war. Diabetes was an opponent worthy of his full effort.

Banting had returned to Toronto. There, he had set up a medical practice while continuing his medical studies at the University of Toronto. One day, he met an old friend and fellow doctor, Joe Gilchrist. Though he knew that Joe was suffering from diabetes, he was still shocked to see how the poor fellow was wasting away. "What are they doing to help you, Joe?" he asked sympathetically.

"They're torturing me," Joe replied. "No one knows what causes the disease, nor does anyone know how to treat it. All we do know is that suddenly the body is no longer able to use up all the sugar and starch it takes in. I'm always hungry and thirsty, yet I know that the more food I eat, the quicker I'll die. My only prescription from the doctors is to starve myself. But I just don't seem to have a chance. Either I eat more food than my body can convert into fuel— or I gradually starve myself to death."

After Banting had left Joe Gilchrist, he couldn't forget what he had seen and heard. He was unable to go about his normal routine because the image of Joe remained constantly in his mind. He knew that scientists had searched for years for a cure for diabetes, with no success. How could *he* hope to find what so many more learned men had failed to find? But he *had* to try!

He read all the material he could get on the subject. It was known that diabetes resulted from some defect in the *pancreas,* the gland that furnishes the digestive juices by which the body turns sugar and starch into energy fuel. As Banting pondered over the problem, he began to sense that a diabetic's pancreas must stop producing enough of these juices, thereby disturbing the body's healthy balance. Why not obtain these same juices from an animal's pancreas and inject them into the human body? It was a simple idea— perhaps too simple to work.

Banting went to visit Dr. MacLeod, director of the university's laboratory. "Dr. MacLeod," he said, "I must have ten dogs and an assistant to help me conduct an important experiment. I think I may be able to solve the problem of diabetes."

"You—*what?* My dear fellow, do you know how many times this has been tried before?"

"Yes, sir, I do," Banting replied. "But I think I've hit on something new. I must have a chance to find out whether it will work."

Dr. MacLeod was skeptical; but he had the open mind of the true scientist. He decided to give the young man a chance. "All right, Dr. Banting. You may have ten dogs and an assistant. Experiment all you like."

Fred Banting gave up his medical practice. He went to work as a self-appointed, unpaid researcher in a laboratory, almost bare of any equipment. He was lucky, though, to have as his assistant a brilliant young medical student, Charles H. Best, who was especially gifted in chemistry. They made a perfect team—Banting doing the surgical work, Best conducting the chemical tests. Together, they worked tirelessly on their dogs, the number of animals rising from ten to ninety-one. But still no results.

Then they injected a fluid into the ninety-second dog, who lay dying of diabetes. Shortly afterwards, Best let out a jubilant cry, "The sugar content in his blood has decreased!" A few hours later, the dog was bounding about the room, barking happily. The two scientists almost barked for joy, too.

But the problem was far from solved. In a few weeks, the dog died. It was then that Banting realized that this fluid, which he had named *insulin,* must be injected daily to maintain the proper functioning of a diabetic pancreas. Though insulin could not cure diabetes, it could *control* it effectively for an indefinite period of time.

Banting was now ready to test insulin on a man. Joe Gilchrist was a willing guinea pig—a dying man eager to grasp at any straw that might possibly save him. But Banting warned him: "Remember, Joe, I can't guarantee that my insulin will have the same

effect on you as it did on the dog. It may even kill
you. Are you willing to take the chance?"

Gilchrist nodded. Banting injected him with insulin.
They would have to wait a few hours before results
were evident. Best took a sample of Gilchrist's blood,
and bent over his test tubes to analyze the contents of
the blood. Gilchrist sat in silence. After a lapse, Best
said quietly, "Sorry, but the sugar content is still extremely high."

Banting was heartbroken. Gilchrist tried to reassure
him: "Don't take it so hard, Fred. At least you didn't
kill me. And you'll find out what's wrong—and lick
it yet!"

Banting went home. He was tired, discouraged. As
he sat at his desk brooding, he suddenly heard a loud
knock at his door and a man's voice shouting.

"Fred, Fred! It worked!" It was Joe Gilchrist. He
excitedly explained to Banting that the insulin had
simply been longer in taking effect than they had
expected. "Your insulin is an elixir of life," he said.
"It has put new energy into my body, and I feel like
a different man."

Much work still lay ahead, but Banting now knew
that he and Best could beat the disease, First, he found
a way of obtaining insulin from the insides of slaugh-
tered cattle—from the parts that butchers were discard-
ing as rubbish. Thus, he was able to produce insulin
in large enough quantities at little expense.

"Fred! Fred! It worked!"

Dr. MacLeod was very impressed. Now he took personal charge of the project and arranged to have a ward set up where diabetics could be treated with the new miracle fluid. Thousands of patients whose cases had been given up as hopeless streamed to Dr. Banting for treatment, even though there was still some danger involved. Banting had not yet been able to establish the exact amount of insulin that should be used for each injection. If too much insulin were given, immediate death might ensue; and Banting could only determine the proper balance by experimenting on these patients.

The diabetics submitted willingly—for without insulin, what hope had they? Eventually, this final problem was surmounted. Joe Gilchrist lived, as have many millions of diabetics since then. Banting's discovery of insulin was hailed throughout the world as few scientific discoveries ever have been.

Honors were heaped upon Banting. In 1922, he and Dr. MacLeod were jointly awarded the Nobel Prize for Medicine—the highest honor the world can bestow on a scientist. Banting immediately sent half his prize to Charles Best with this message: "You are with me in my share—always."

ALBERT EINSTEIN

(1879-1955)

Greatest Genius of Our Time

THROUGH THE open window of a yellow frame house came the strains of beautiful violin music. Then the violin stopped playing and a kindly old man, wearing an old woolen sweater and smoking a pipe, appeared at the door. He smiled and waved to the children who passed his house on their way to school.

No one asked the name of that gentle violinist— for his face was familiar to millions. He was the greatest scientist of our century, and one of the supreme thinkers of all time.

Driven from Germany by the Nazis because he was Jewish, Albert Einstein found a haven of freedom in the United States. During the last twenty-two years of his life, in the calm, scholarly atmosphere of the uni-

For that simple-looking equation was the key which unlocked...one of Nature's greatest secrets.

versity town of Princeton, New Jersey, he studied and taught and brought his precedent-shattering theories to final fruition.

Although but a handful of brilliant men understood the complicated mathematical formulas which expressed his revolutionary theory of relativity, every one of us has been affected by the results. Einstein not only modified Newton's gravitational laws, but altered our conception of the universe. He wrote a simple-looking equation—$E = mc^2$—which was to launch the age of atomic energy.

For that simple-looking equation was the key which unlocked the door to the discovery of one of Nature's greatest secrets: how to release the immense energy stored within the tiny atom.

Before Einstein died in April, 1955, his mighty mind had grappled with the basics of the universe; he attempted to explain all known phenomena with a single set of mathematical equations. The immense effect of his far-reaching theories on scientific research may not be crystallized for years to come, but all scientists are agreed that Einstein was a genius the like of which may not appear again for generations. He has been hailed as the greatest intellect of our age!

HART

PUBLISHING

COMPANY